Intermediate Repertoire 1

by James and Jane Smisor Bastien

KJOS WEST • Neil A. Kjos Music Co., Publisher • San Diego, California

PREFACE

The INTERMEDIATE PIANO COURSE is designed to be used after the student has completed Level 4 of the BASTIEN PIANO LIBRARY. In addition, the INTERMEDIATE PIANO COURSE may be used by a student who has completed *any* elementary piano course. This course is a comprehensive, organized program of study consisting of four books per level which may be used simultaneously for best results. The INTERMEDIATE PIANO COURSE is available in grade levels 1, 2, 3, in each of the following books.

- INTERMEDIATE REPERTOIRE
- INTERMEDIATE THEORY
- INTERMEDIATE TECHNIC
- INTERMEDIATE MULTI-KEY SOLOS

INTERMEDIATE REPERTOIRE introduces the student to many factors of each style period: Baroque, Classical, Romantic, and Contemporary. For each period there are descriptions of overall styles (dress, art, architecture), keyboard instruments, various compositions representative of each period, and a list of composers. The music is a combination of master composer works and pieces written by the Bastiens in each style period. Special emphasis is given to providing more accessible pieces in the Romantic style. The teacher may assign pieces from different periods of the Repertoire book at the same time.

INTERMEDIATE THEORY contains written and playing material to coordinate with the Repertoire book.

INTERMEDIATE TECHNIC contains exercises and etudes by the standard composers as well as many new studies by the Bastiens.

INTERMEDIATE MULTI-KEY SOLOS provides a variety of original music by the Bastiens to encourage the student to explore many keys rather than staying in the limited key selection found in master composer works at the intermediate level.

The INTERMEDIATE PIANO COURSE includes the following books:

Intermediate Repertoire 1 (WP105)
Intermediate Repertoire 2 (WP106)
Intermediate Repertoire 3 (WP107)

Intermediate Theory 1 (WP108)
Intermediate Theory 2 (WP109)
Intermediate Theory 3 (WP110)

Intermediate Technic 1 (WP111)
Intermediate Technic 2 (WP112)
Intermediate Technic 3 (WP113)

Intermediate Multi-key Solos 1 (WP114)
Intermediate Multi-key Solos 2 (WP115)
Intermediate Multi-key Solos 3 (WP116)

Printed in USA.
ISBN #0-8497-5186-1

On the cover is one of many sea anemones (a sedentary marine animal with a columnar body and circles of tentacles surrounding the mouth) found in the Pacific Ocean.

CONTENTS

Hoe Down

STYLE: CONTEMPORARY (American Square Dance)

JAMES BASTIEN

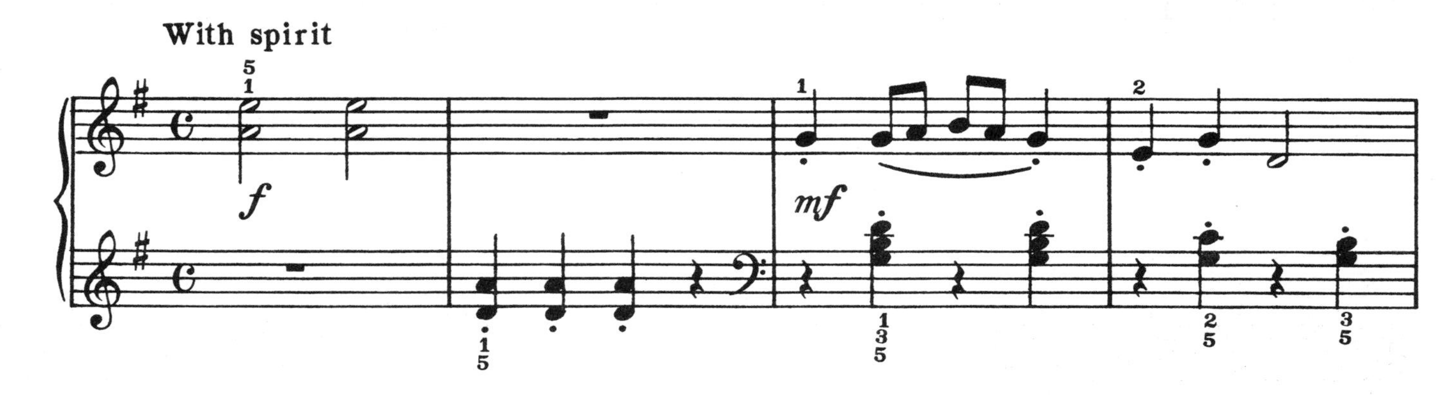

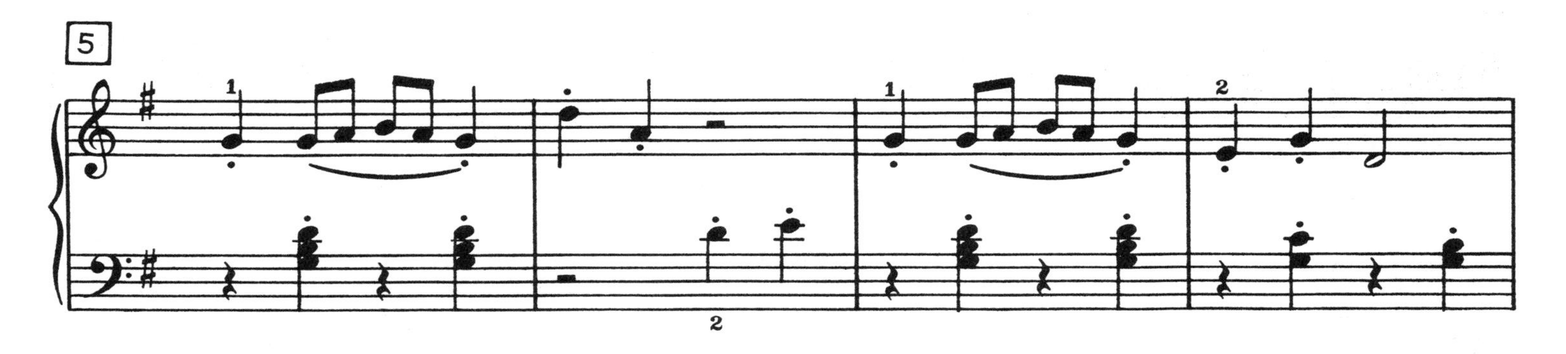

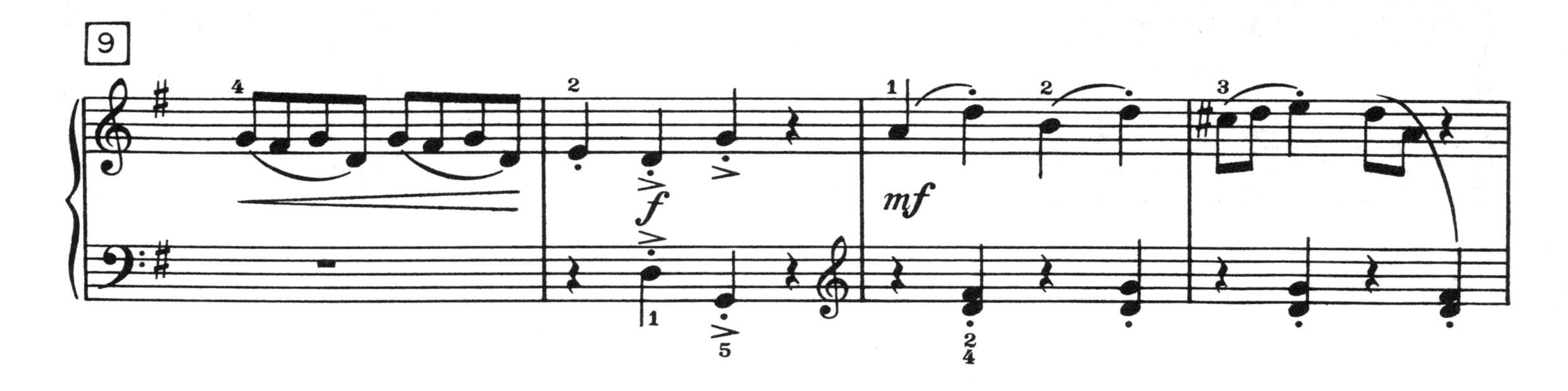

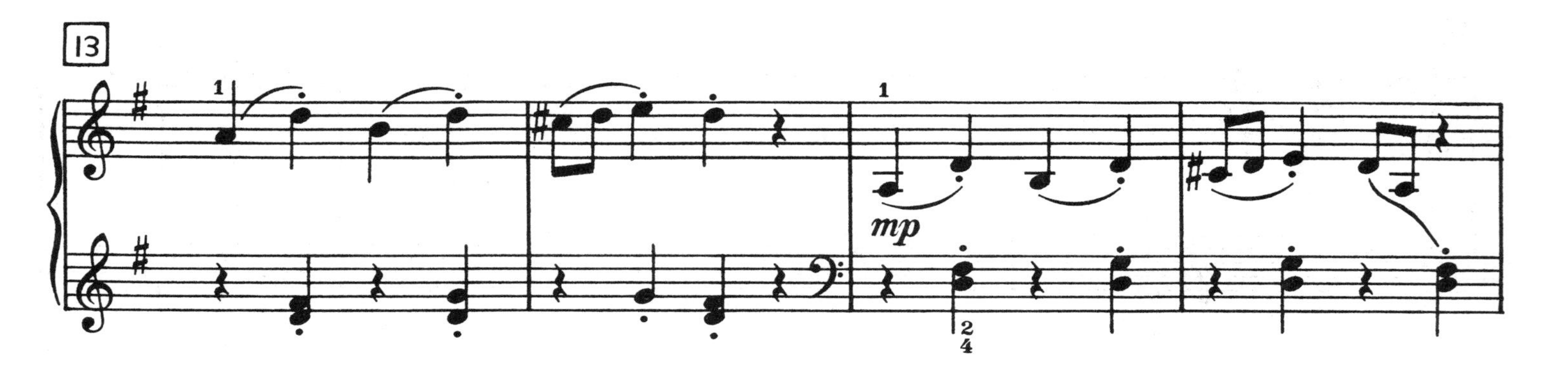

17
f
21
mf
25
f
29
f
p
f

Triplet Rhythm (review*)

A triplet eighth note figure is equal to one quarter note: 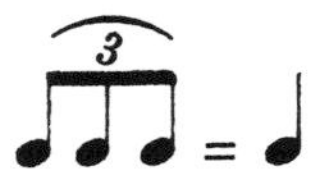

Clap and count this rhythm.

Etude in Triplets

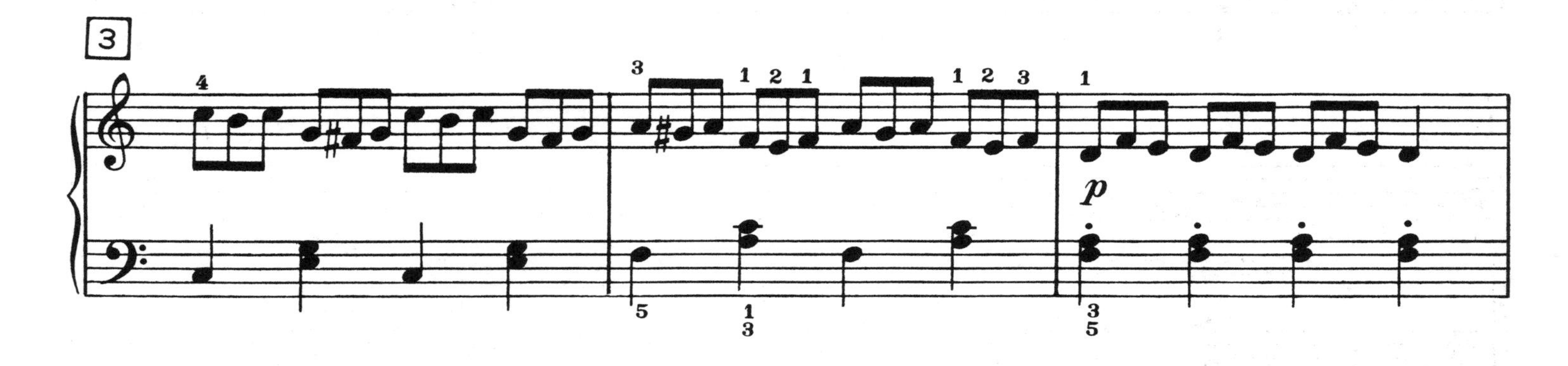

*Introduced in Level 3 of THE BASTIEN PIANO LIBRARY.

Desert Caravan

STYLE: CONTEMPORARY

JAMES BASTIEN

THE BAROQUE PERIOD

"Assumption of St. Mary"
by Peter Paul Rubens (1577-1640)

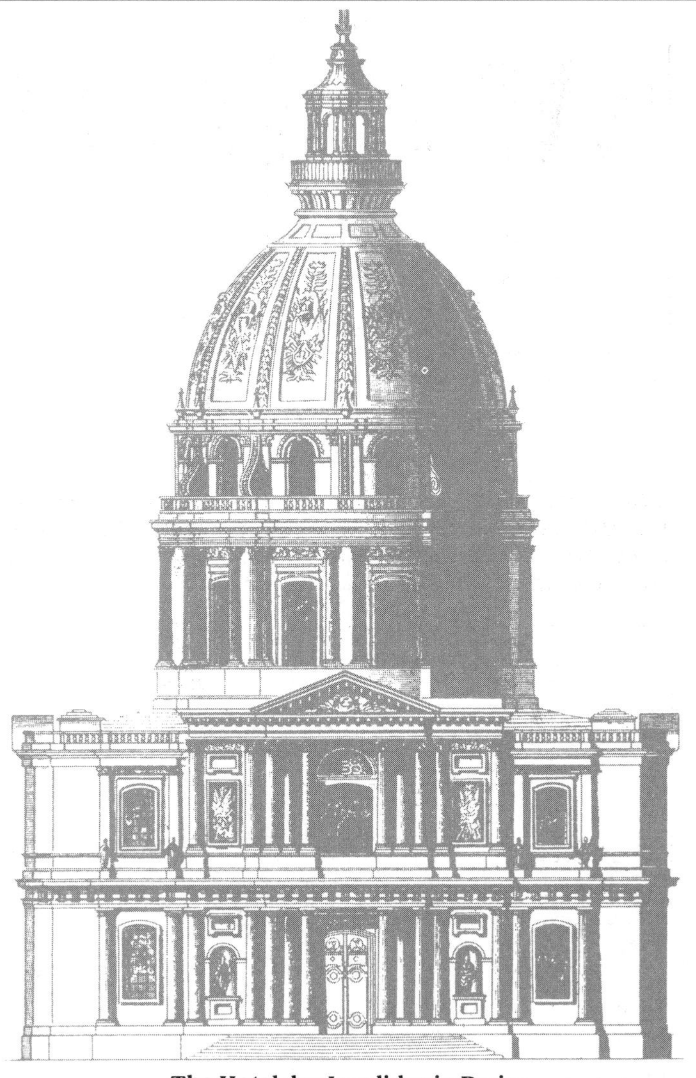

The Hotel des Invalides in Paris

Baroque Style

The Baroque period was a time in history (1600-1750) which had certain styles, customs, and characteristics. During this time people wore fancy clothes with lots of ruffles and decorations, and they also wore powdered wigs with many waves and curls. The art and architecture of this period also incorporated many ornamental decorations. Churches, palaces, and other buildings often were built on a large scale design and included much detail work.

Baroque Keyboard Music

The keyboard music in the Baroque period was frequently written in *two parts,* sometimes called *voices* (single notes in each hand).

from Passepied by Handel

A melody often consists of a short pattern (called a *motive*) which is repeated throughout a piece. One or more motives may be used in the composition.

from Air in D minor by Purcell

1600-1750

Baroque Forms

Much of the music was written as dance pieces such as the *minuet, march, gavotte, gigue,* and many others. Each dance has its own rhythm and style.

Baroque music often was written in *binary,* or two-part form. The two parts are called section A and section B, and usually each section is repeated: ‖: A :‖: B :‖

Baroque Keyboard Instruments

Before the invention of the piano, keyboard music was written for the *clavichord* and the *harpsichord.* The clavichord produces a small delicate sound and was used mainly in small rooms where it could be heard. The harpsichord has a bigger sound and was the favored instrument during the Baroque period. It is still popular today.

18th Century German Clavichord
From the Metropolitan Museum of Art, The Crosby Brown Collection of Musical Instruments, 1889.

18th Century French Harpsichord
From the Metropolitan Museum of Art, Gift of Susan Dwight Bliss, 1944.

Baroque Composers

The two best known Baroque composers are Johann Sebastian Bach (1685-1750) and George Frideric Handel (1685-1759), both Germans. The best known English composer from the Baroque period is Henry Purcell (1659-1695). Antonio Vivaldi (1678-1741) and Domenico Scarlatti (1685-1757) are two of the most famous Baroque Italian composers. Well known French Baroque composers include Jean Baptiste Lully (1632-1687), Françoise Couperin (1668-1733), and Jean-Philippe Rameau (1683-1764).

Bach, Scarlatti, Rameau, and Couperin wrote a great deal of music for the harpsichord. Their keyboard music is played frequently in concerts today on either a piano or a harpsichord.

The gavotte (pronounced ga-vaht') is a lively French dance. It is in $\frac{4}{4}$ meter and usually begins on the third beat:

Gavotte

STYLE: BAROQUE

JAMES BASTIEN

The bourrée (pronounced boor-ay') is a lively French dance. It is in $\frac{2}{2}$ meter and usually begins with an upbeat: either ♩|♩ or ♫|♩

Bourrée

STYLE: BAROQUE

JAMES BASTIEN

Johann Sebastian Bach (1685-1750), a German composer, had numerous relatives who were musicians: from seven generations, 193 out of 200 were musicians. Bach's parents died when he was 10 years old, and his oldest brother, Johann Christopher, raised him. His brother died when Johann Sebastian was 15. Following that, Johann Sebastian lived at the St. Michael School where he studied music and was a choirboy. At 19, Bach obtained a position as organist at a church in Arnstadt. Throughout his life he held positions at various churches and in royal courts, and for almost 30 years he was director of music at the St. Michael School in Leipzig. He was married twice and had 20 children, several of whom became well-known musicians. On his second wife's 25th birthday, he gave her (Anna Magdalena) a notebook containing pieces for members of his family to play. His best known easier clavier pieces come from this notebook. Bach was a prolific composer; his complete works fill 46 large volumes containing choral music, concertos, orchestral and chamber works, and organ and clavier music.

The minuet is a French dance in $\frac{3}{4}$ meter at a moderate (or moderately fast) pace.

Minuet in G Major

from "Notebook for Anna Magdalena"

STYLE: BAROQUE

J.S. BACH

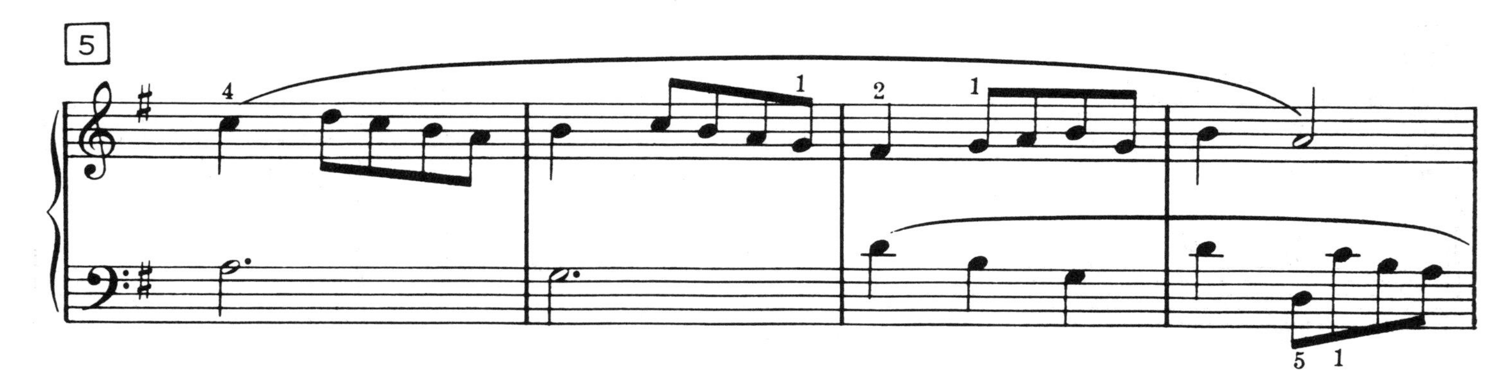

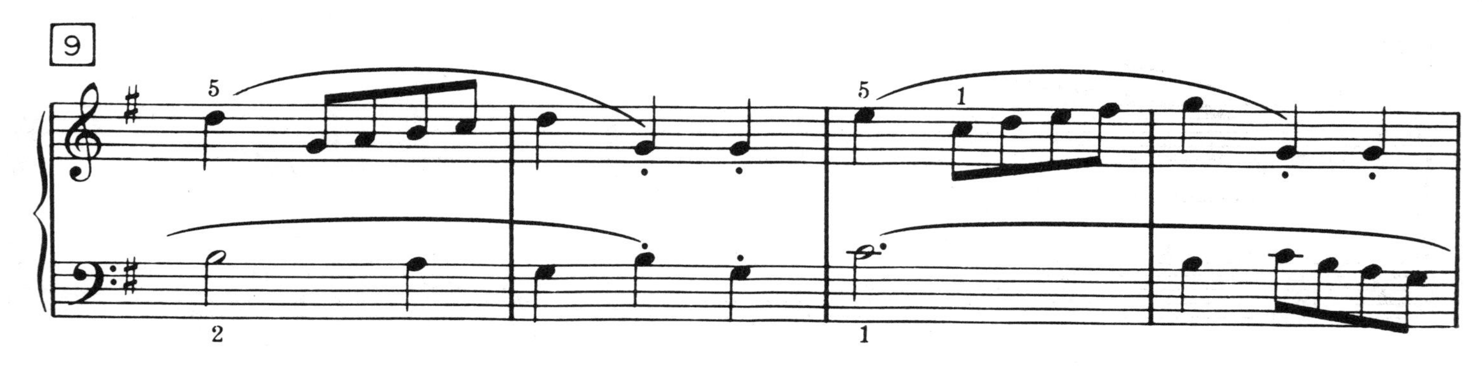

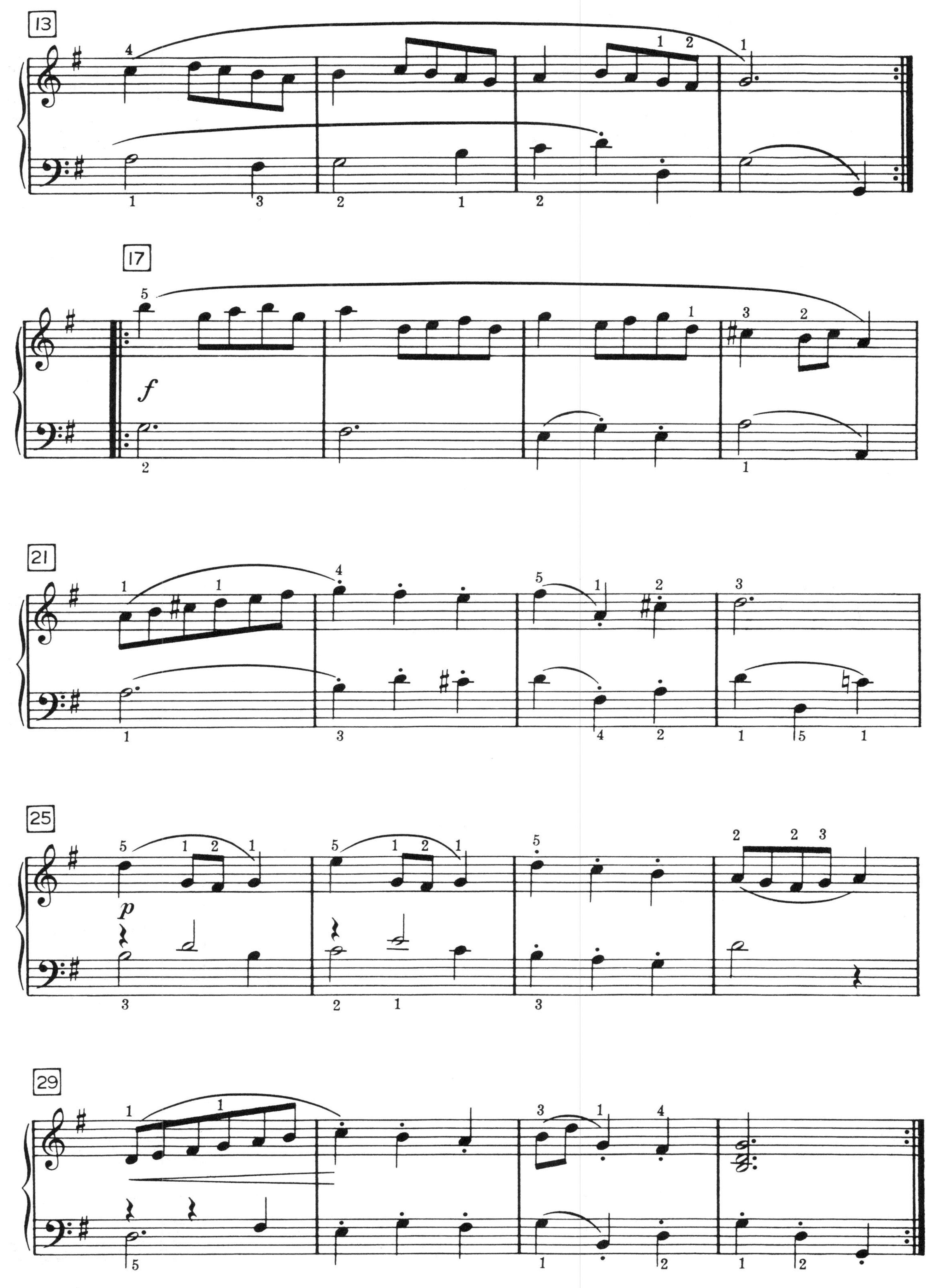
13
17
21
25
29

The aria is a song of lyrical character found in operas and other vocal works.

Aria in F Major

from "Notebook for Anna Magdalena"

STYLE: BAROQUE

J.S. BACH

Jean-Baptiste Lully (1632-1687) lived his first 14 years in Florence, Italy. He then moved to Paris where he soon mastered the French language and adapted to French customs. He entered the service of Louis XIV at the age of 20, and he remained in court employment for the rest of his life. Lully was largely responsible for development of the French opera, which was quite an accomplishment for an Italian-born musician. He mainly wrote operas and ballets and some instrumental music.

Minuet in D Minor

STYLE: BAROQUE

JEAN-BAPTISTE LULLY

Sixteenth Note Rhythm (review*)

A single sixteenth note receives one-fourth of a beat when a quarter note receives one beat

A single sixteenth note has two flags. 𝅘𝅥𝅯

Two or more sixteenth notes are connected by a double beam. 

2/4	3/4	4/4	Time Signatures
𝅘𝅥𝅯 = 1/4 beat		𝄿 = 1/4 beat rest	
two sixteenths = 1/2 beat		𝄾 = 1/2 beat rest	
four sixteenths = 1 beat		𝄽 = 1 beat rest	

Play the group of four sixteenths evenly between beats as you count aloud. You may find it helpful to say "and" between the beats.

Clap and count the following rhythm.

Count aloud while you play the following Etudes. Transpose to other keys.

Sixteenth Note Etudes

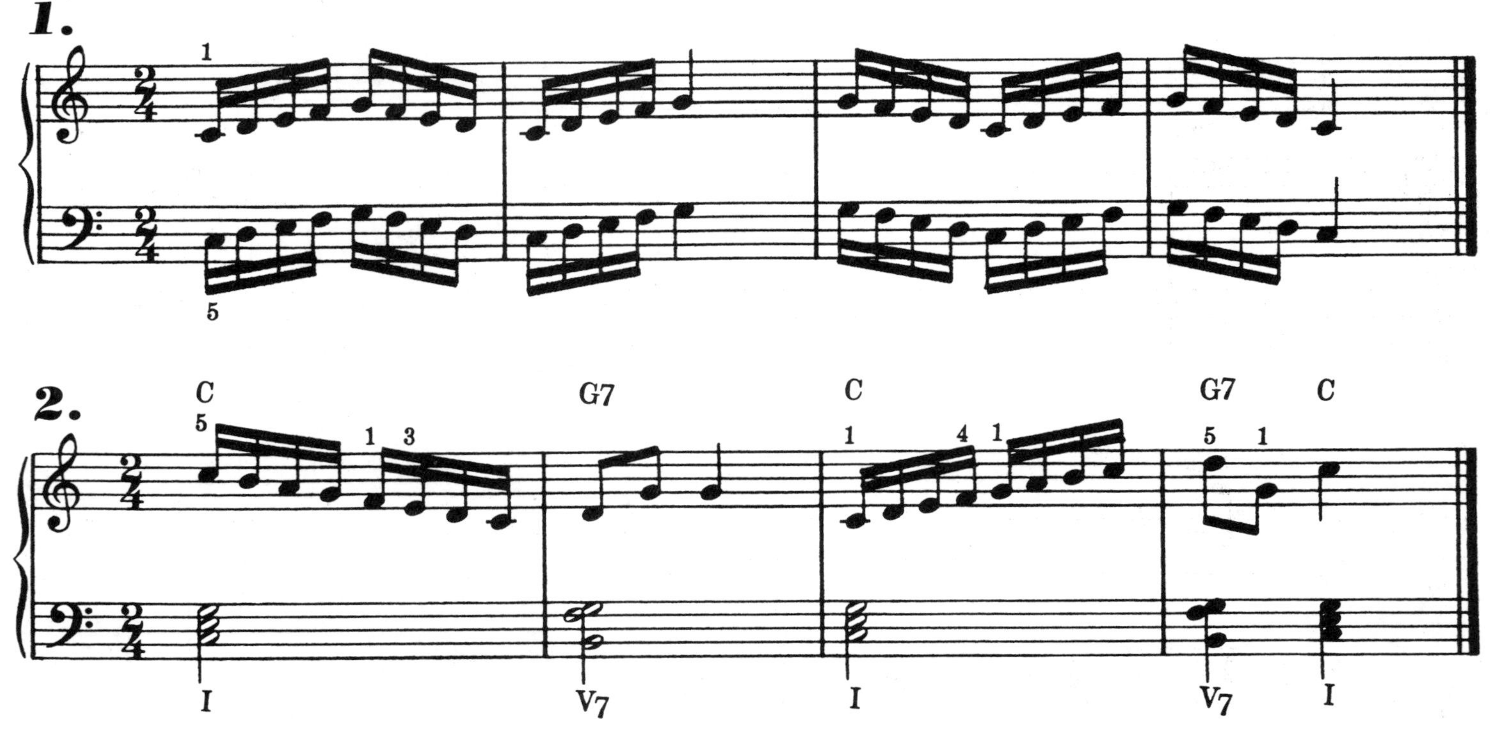

*Introduced in Level 4 of THE BASTIEN PIANO LIBRARY.

Etude Allegro

JAMES BASTIEN

THE CLASSICAL PERIOD

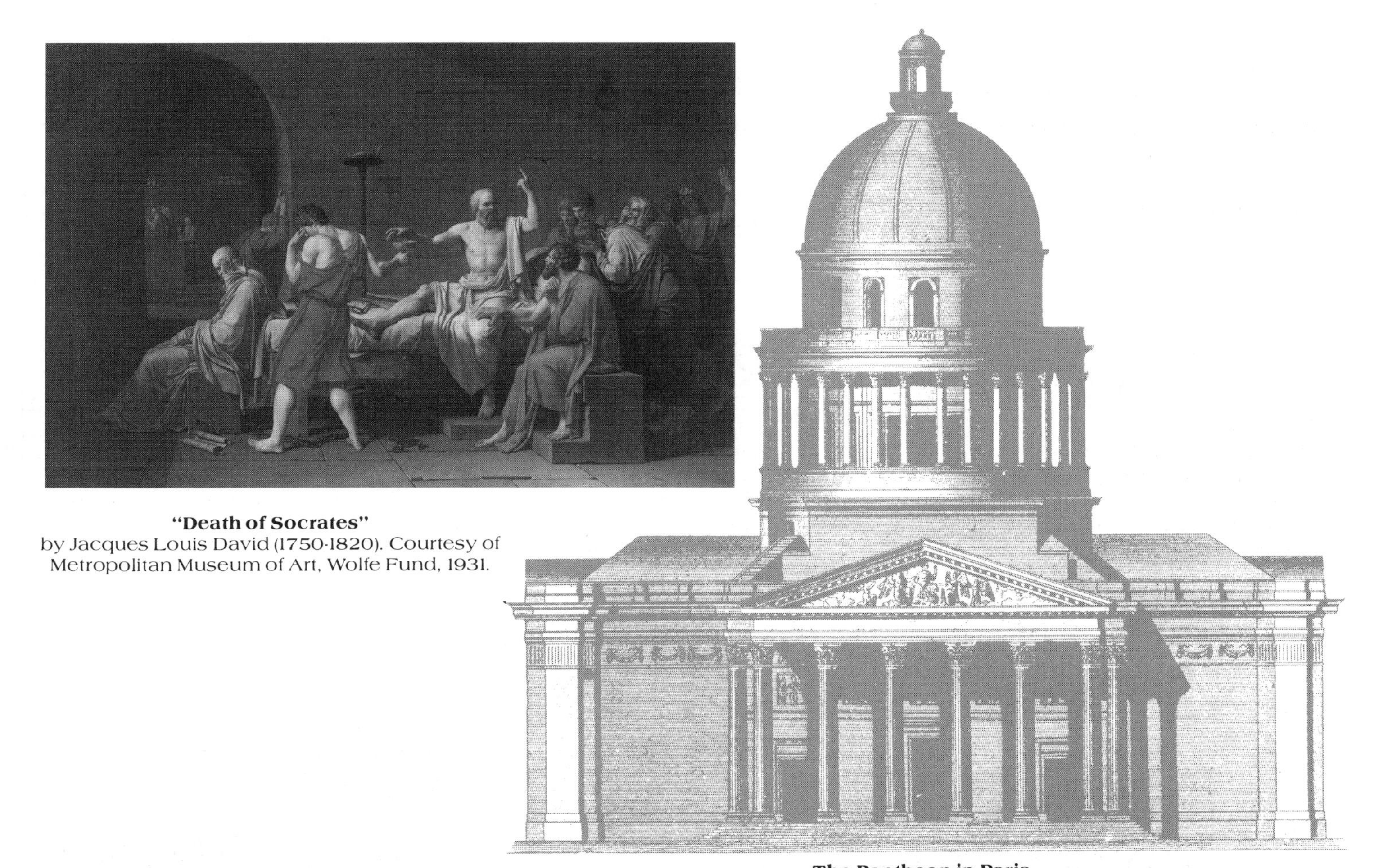

"Death of Socrates"
by Jacques Louis David (1750-1820). Courtesy of Metropolitan Museum of Art, Wolfe Fund, 1931.

The Pantheon in Paris

Classical Style

The Classical period, dating from about 1750-1820, was a time of change from the decorative Baroque to a more simple style. People wore clothes that were tailored in a less complicated manner than in the Baroque period and people stopped wearing wigs with fancy stylings. The art and architecture of the period also reflected many of these changes. Buildings were built with simple, graceful, "classical" lines defined by balanced form.

Classical Keyboard Music

The keyboard music in the Classical period was frequently written in balanced phrase groupings lasting two, four, or eight measures.

from Minuet in C by Mozart

The style of writing often consists of a solo line with chordal accompaniment, rather than the two-voice style of the Baroque.

from Écossaise in G by Beethoven.

1750-1820

Classical Forms

Although dance pieces (minuet, etc.) were still written in the Classical period, expanded forms such as the *sonata allegro* and the *rondo* emerged.

In the first movements of sonatas and sonatinas ("little" sonatas), the form is usually *ternary*, or three-part form. The three parts are called *exposition* (A), *development* (B), and *recapitulation* (A): A B A.

The Early Piano

Credit is given to the Italian, Bartolomeo Cristofori, for producing the first piano in 1709. He was curator of musical instruments for the wealthy Medici family in Florence. At about the same time, other people had also invented the piano: Marius in France (1716) and Schröter in Germany (1717). Cristofori called his invention a *gravicembalo col piano e forte* (a keyboard instrument that can play soft and loud). The ability of the early piano to produce graded dynamics (crescendos and decrescendos), plus its light, silvery tone and sustaining quality was a tremendous change from the clavichord and harpsichord.

Grand Pianoforte by Muzio Clementi, 1801
From the Collection of James K. and Peggy F. Baird, Huntsville, Alabama

Italian Pianoforte by Bartolomeo Cristofori, 1720
From the Metropolitan Museum of Art, The Crosby Brown Collection of Musical Instruments, 1889.

Classical Composers

The three most famous classical composers are Franz Joseph Haydn (1732-1809), Wolfgang Amadeus Mozart (1756-1791), and Ludwig van Beethoven (1770-1827). All three composers either studied or lived in Vienna, Austria. The Italian, Muzio Clementi (1752-1832) is another composer from this period now best remembered for his keyboard sonatinas.

These four composers wrote a great deal of piano music which they performed themselves. Mozart, Beethoven, and Clementi were especially prominent as pianists.

Minuet

STYLE: CLASSICAL

JAMES BASTIEN

Allegro in C

STYLE: CLASSICAL
JANE SMISOR BASTIEN
Allegro
f
mf
mp
f
mf
cresc.
ff

Franz Joseph Haydn (1732-1809), an Austrian composer, studied singing, violin, and clavier as a youth and became a choirboy at the Vienna Cathedral. He spent more than 30 years in the service of Prince Esterházy, a Hungarian nobleman, at Eisenstadt. Haydn was a major influence in the development of the symphony, sonata, and string quartet. During his long life he composed approximately 83 string quartets, more than 50 piano sonatas, 200 songs, over 100 symphonies, 18 operas, a vast amount of church music, concertos, and many other works.

Minuet in G

STYLE: CLASSICAL

FRANZ JOSEPH HAYDN

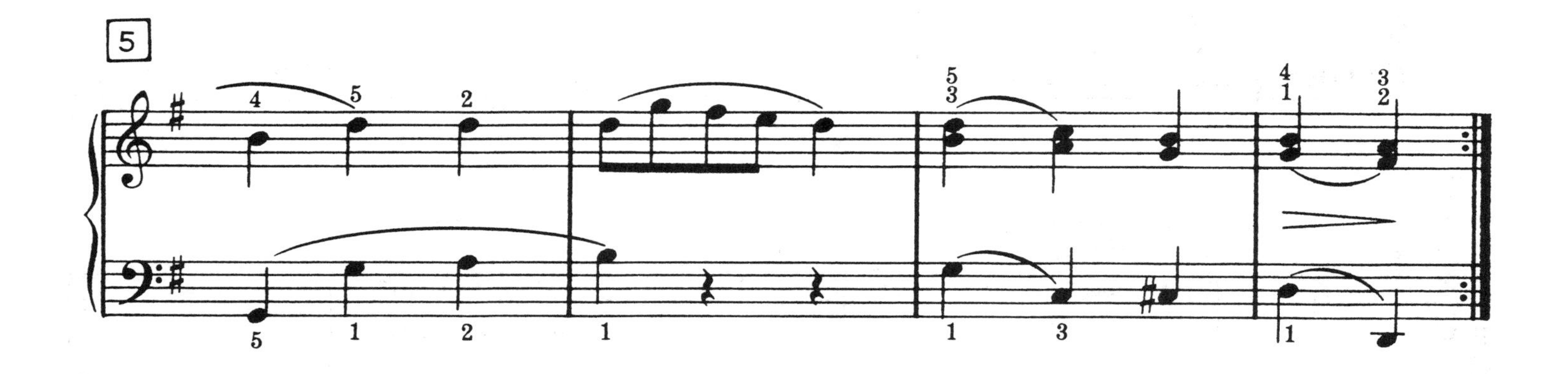

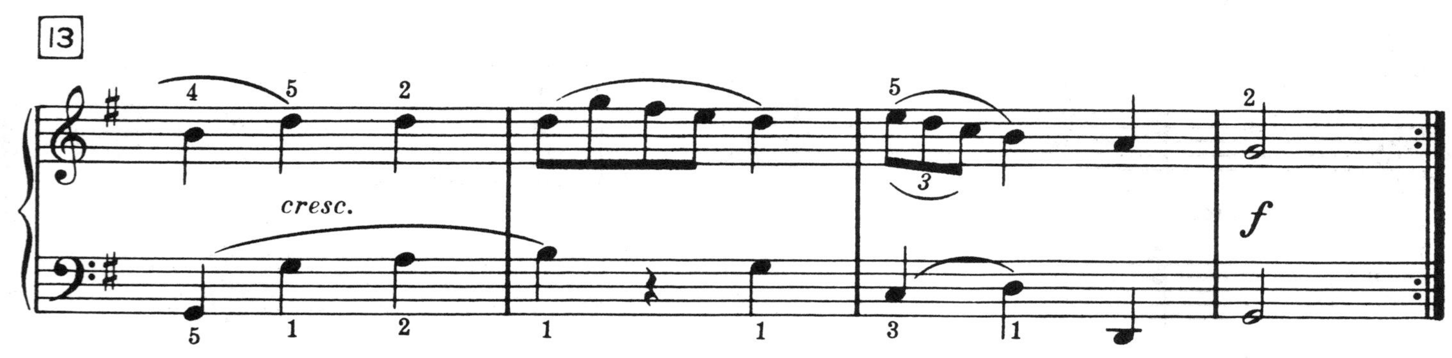

During the 18th century, dance music was played for court functions and informal occasions. The minuet was the most popular during most of the century. However, toward the end of the century the *German dance* emerged in popularity. It is called *Ländler* in German and is a folk dance in $\frac{3}{4}$ meter. It was very popular in the early 19th century, before the waltz came into vogue.

German Dance

Wolfgang Amadeus Mozart (1756-1791), an Austrian composer and pianist, was a child prodigy. He was taught to play the harpsichord and violin by his father, Leopold. By the age of five he could play and compose music. When he was six, his father arranged a debut for Wolfgang and his sister, Nannerl. He then toured all over Europe displaying his remarkable musical ability in performing, sight reading, improvising, and composing. Mozart could write a complete symphony during a stagecoach ride, or write out a complicated score from memory after one hearing. During his brief lifetime, he wrote numerous symphonies, operas, concertos, songs, church music, chamber music, and keyboard music.

Minuet in C

(K. 6)

Minuet in F

(K. 2)

STYLE: CLASSICAL

WOLFGANG AMADEUS MOZART

Ludwig van Beethoven (1770-1827), a German composer, grew up in Bonn where he studied the violin and piano. Beethoven's father, a chapel singer employed by the Archbishop-Elector of Bonn, was a stern taskmaster and drove young Ludwig to long hours of practice hoping he would become a child prodigy like Mozart. Although Beethoven was obviously talented, he did not become a "marketable" child prodigy. In 1787 he visited Vienna where he played for Mozart, who predicted an outstanding musical career for him. Beethoven hurried back to Bonn to attend his mother who became ill. After his mother's death, he remained at Bonn for five years as a viola player in the court opera orchestra. In 1792 he returned to Vienna and studied with Haydn for about a year. Around this time Beethoven began to earn his living from the sale of compositions and from teaching. He became an honored and respected musician to many royal families (Prince Lichnowsky, Count Waldstein, Count Rasumovsky, etc.), and he dedicated many of his works to these noblemen. In his early thirties, Beethoven experienced a hearing loss which later deteriorated into total deafness. The increasing deafness altered his character. He grew morose and suspicious and had frequent outbursts of temper. A prolific composer, Beethoven wrote 32 piano sonatas, five piano concertos, one violin concerto, an opera, a great quantity of chamber music, and many other works.

Russian Folk Song

STYLE: CLASSICAL

LUDWIG VAN BEETHOVEN

The écossaise (a French word pronounced eh′-ko-sehz) belongs to the category of English country dances. It was popular in the early nineteenth century. Both Beethoven and Schubert wrote collections of écossaises, all in lively $\frac{2}{4}$ meters.

Écossaise in G

STYLE: CLASSICAL

LUDWIG VAN BEETHOVEN

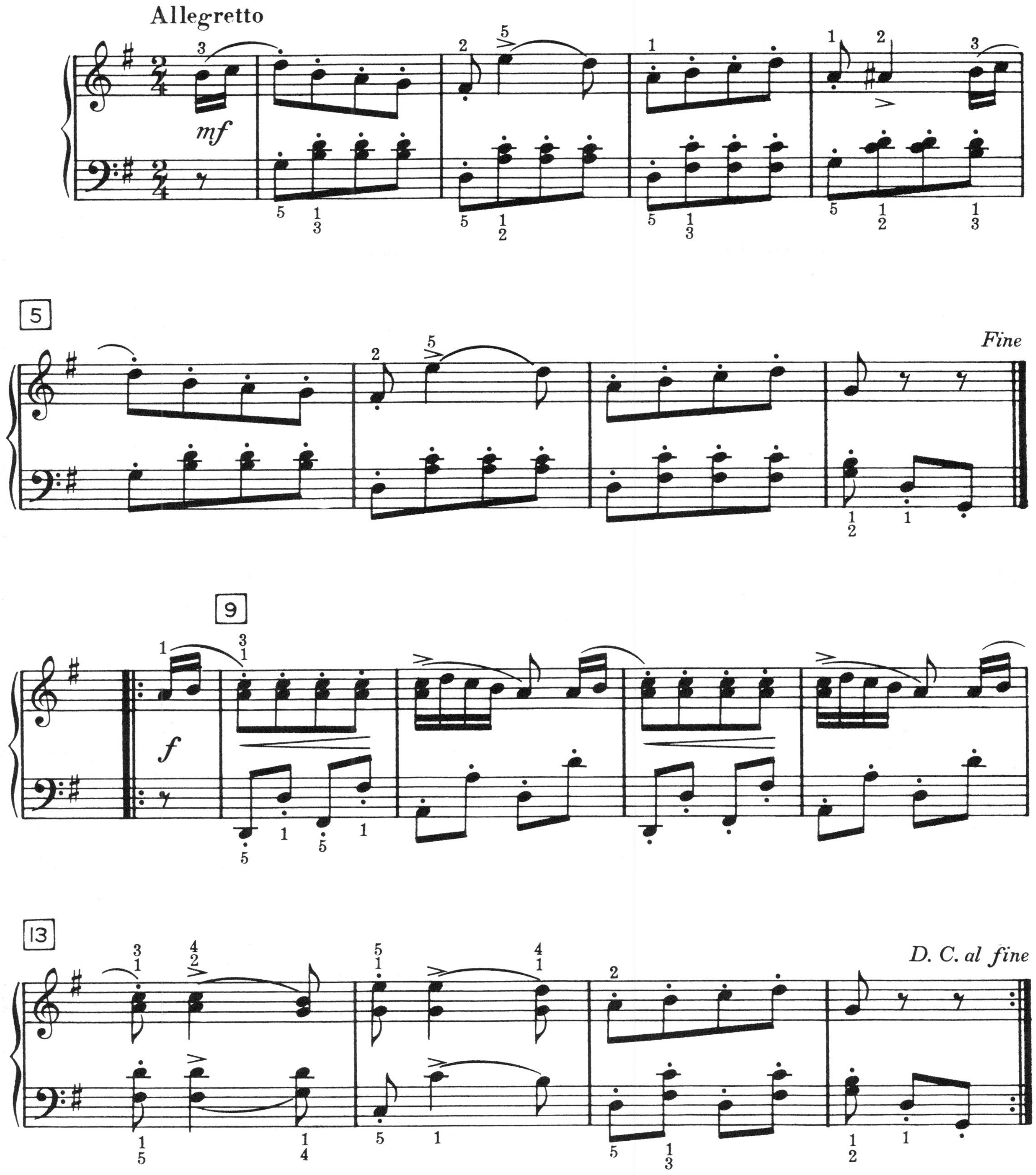

Allegretto

mf

5

Fine

9

f

13

D. C. al fine

The form of a sonatina is often: **A** (first theme) **B** (second theme) **A** (first theme) **Coda.** The second theme usually is contrasting in character to the first theme and in the *dominant* key. Notice how the form is used in this sonatina.

The accompaniment used in this sonatina is a broken-chord figure called the *Alberti bass* (named after Domenico Alberti who was one of the first to use this type of accompaniment).

Practice the left hand alone to identify the chords.

Sonatina

STYLE: CLASSICAL

JAMES BASTIEN

14
Transition
p
cresc.
19
Section A
a tempo
mf
poco rit.
mf
legato
23
27
Coda
f
31
p
f

Triads and Inversions (review*)

A triad in root position has notes which are on either all lines or all spaces.

Any root position triad may be inverted (rearranged) by moving the root note to the top or middle.

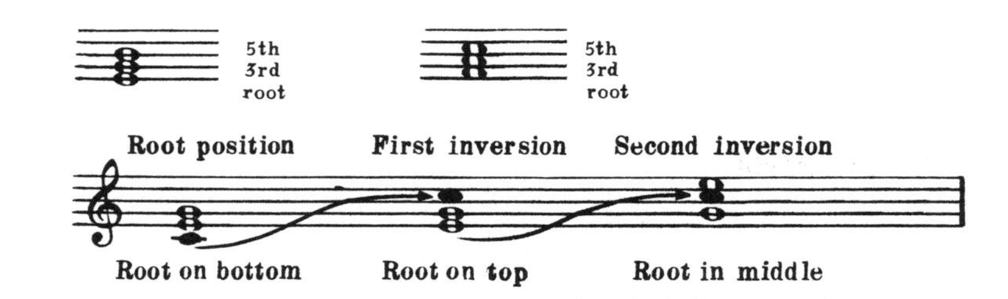

Practice triads and inversions first in major, then in minor (lower the middle note one half step to play minor) Play hands separately at first. Memorize the patterns below with the correct fingerings and play block chord and broken chord styles. Practice in all 12 major and minor triads.

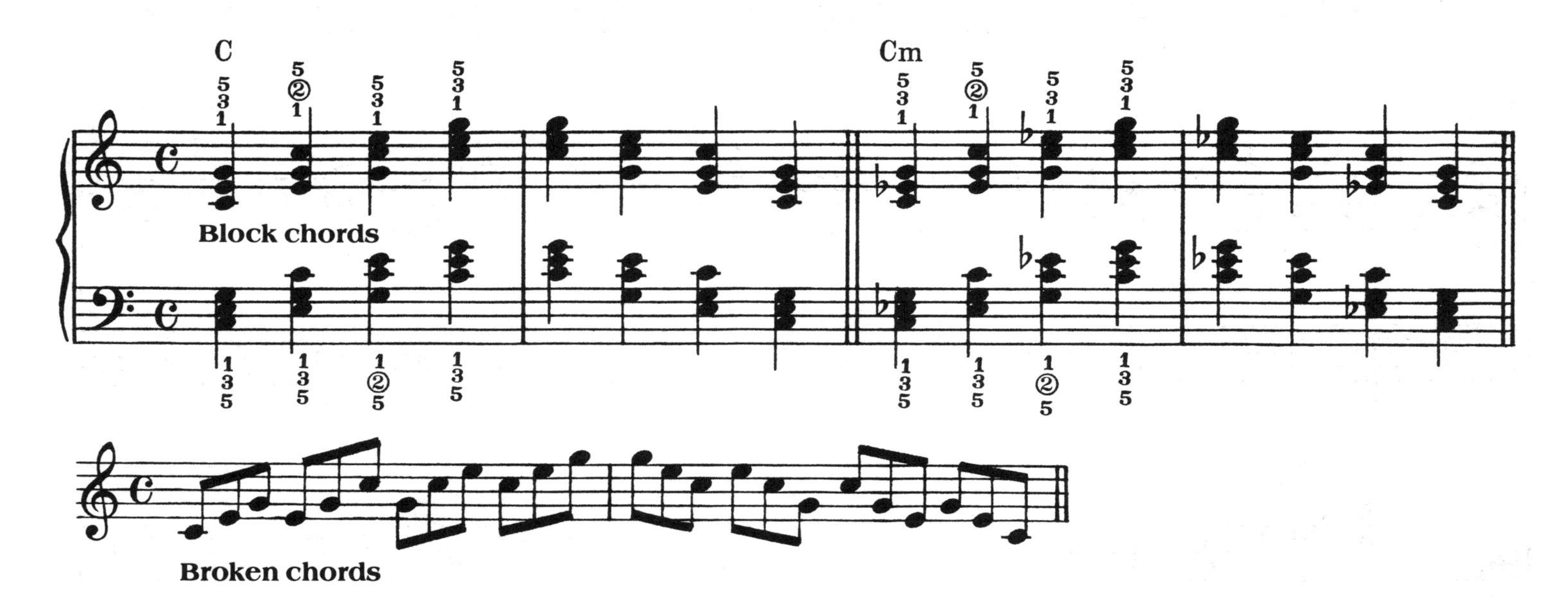

Rhythm Patterns

Three rhythms are given here for further inversion practice. In addition, you might want to make up some of your own. Play either hands separately or hands together.

1. Quarter and eighth note rhythm

2. Dotted rhythm

Count: 1 and 2 and a

3. Syncopated rhythm

Count: 1 and 2 and

*Introduced in Level 3 of THE BASTIEN PIANO LIBRARY.

Celebration March

STYLE: CLASSICAL

JANE SMISOR BASTIEN

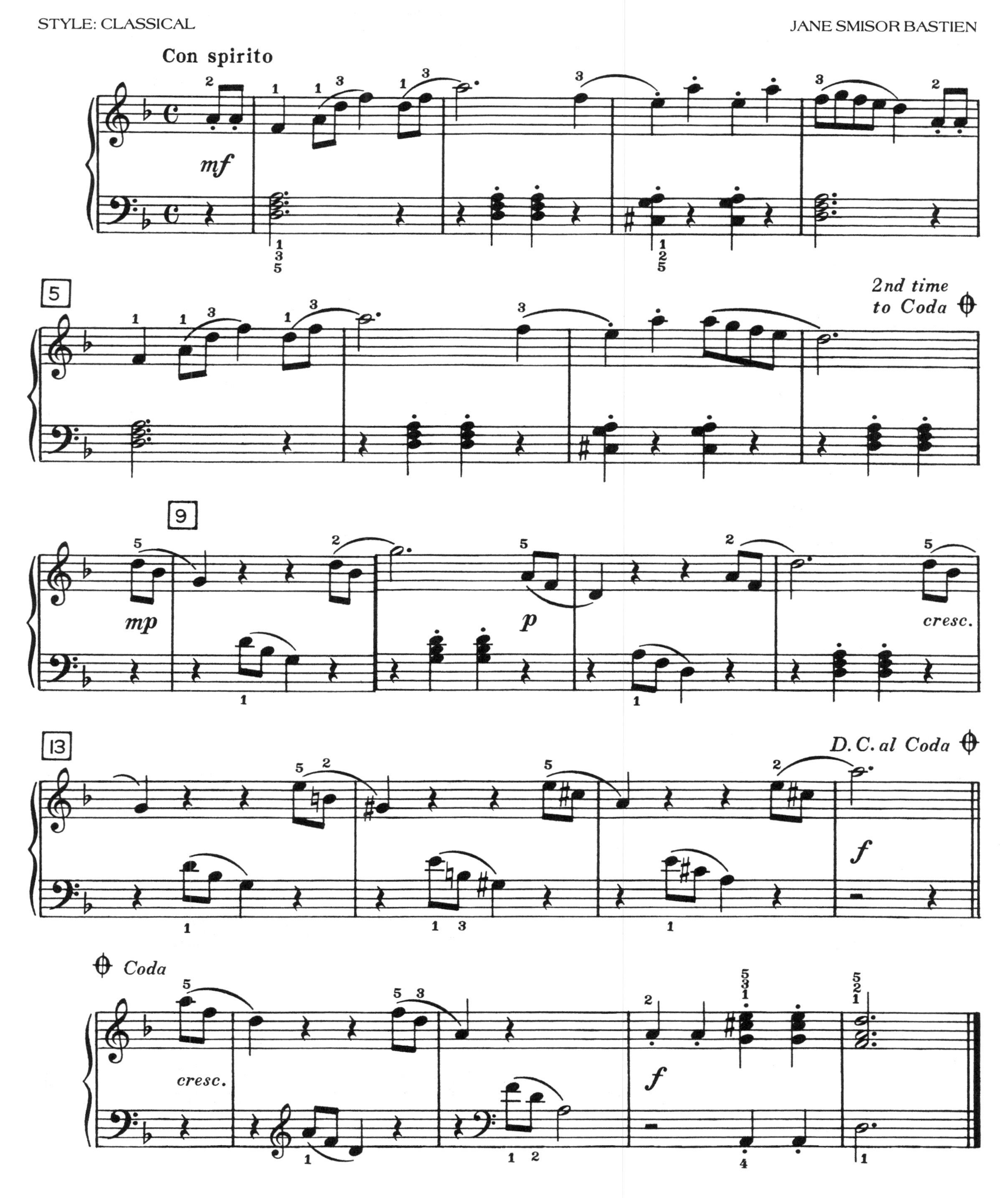

Dominant Seventh Chord and Inversions

A dominant seventh chord (V7) in root position has notes which are on either all lines or all spaces.

Any root position dominant seventh may be inverted by moving the root note in the following manner

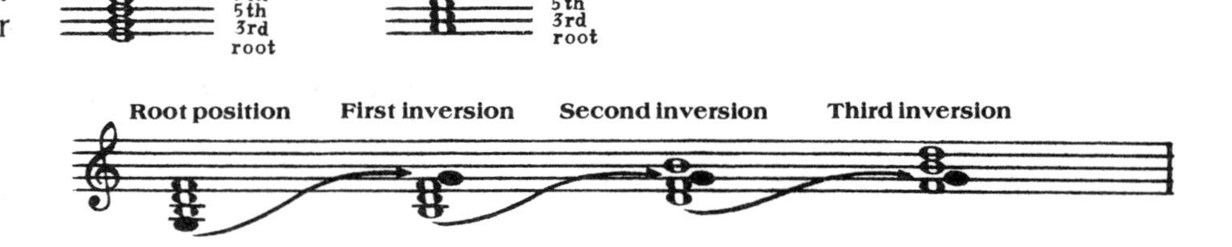

G Dominant Seventh Chord

Practice inversions of the G dominant seventh chord. Play hands separately at first. Memorize the patterns below with the correct fingerings and play block chord and broken chord styles. Note that finger 3 or 4 may be used as indicated depending on the size of your hand.

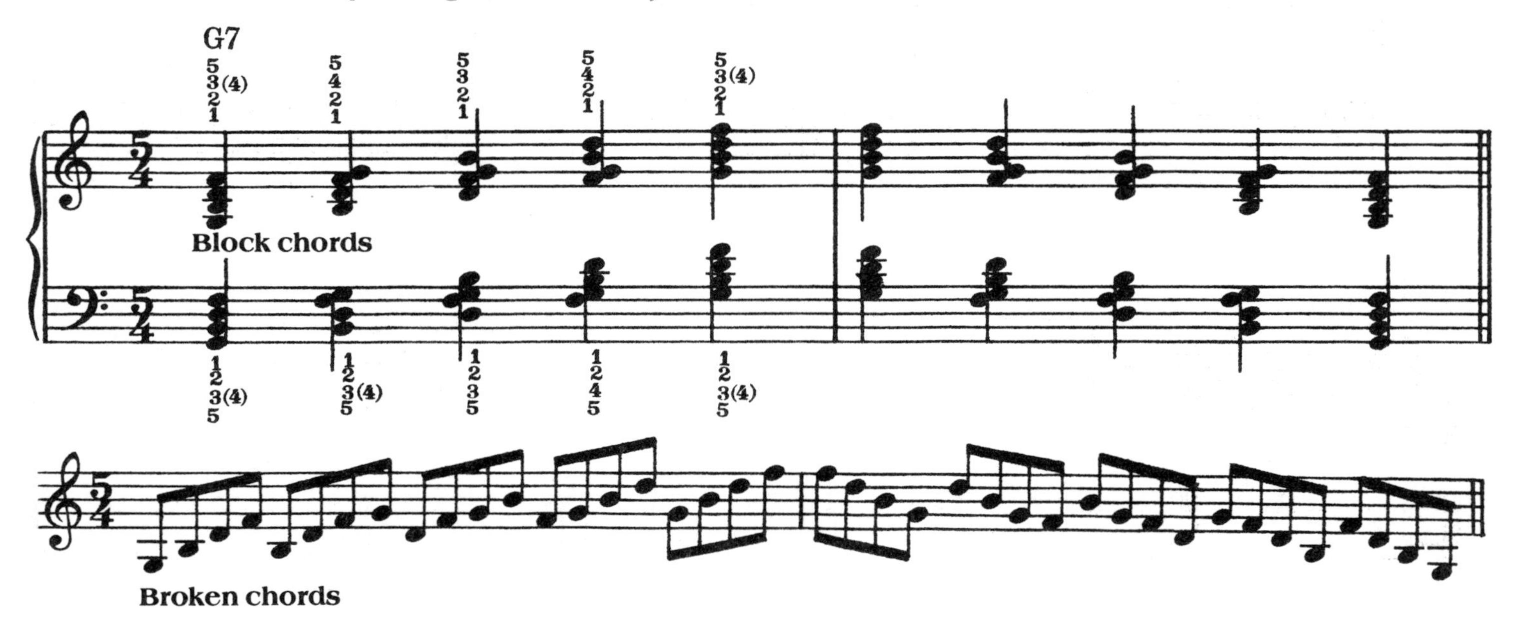

Rhythm Patterns

Three rhythms are given here for further inversion practice. In addition, you might want to make up some of your own.

D Dominant Seventh Chord

Practice the D dominant seventh chord in the ways shown above.

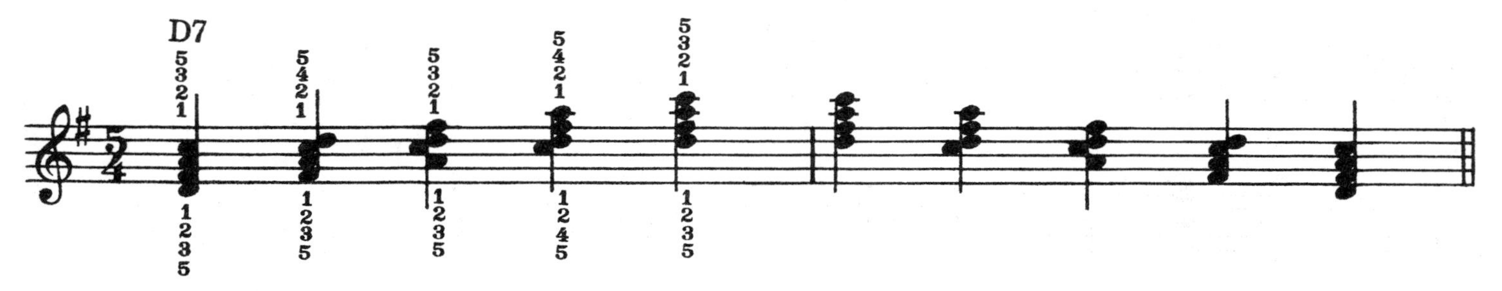

Anton Diabelli (1781-1858), Austrian composer and publisher, taught piano and guitar until he became owner of Diabelli and Company, his publishing firm. He published a large portion of Schubert's works. Beethoven wrote a set of variations on a theme by Diabelli which did a great deal to immortalize Diabelli's name.

The bagatelle (pronounced ba-ga-tel') is a French word meaning "trifle." Usually written for piano, the bagatelle is a short piece having a light character.

Bagatelle

STYLE: CLASSICAL

ANTON DIABELLI

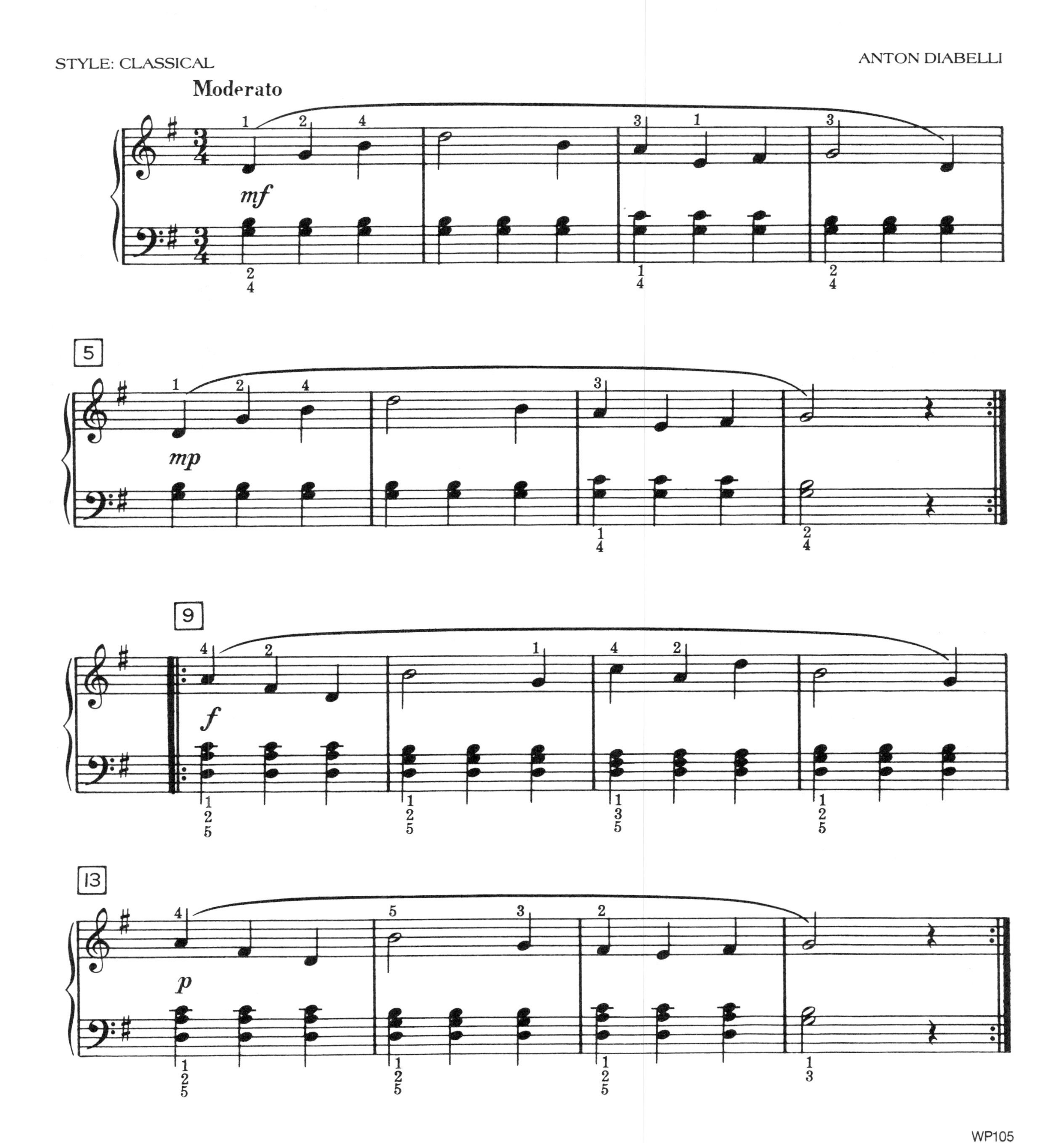

THE ROMANTIC PERIOD

"Stoke-by-Nayland"
by John Constable (1836). Courtesy of
The Art Institute of Chicago.

The Papal Cancellaria in Rome

Romantic Style

The Romantic period dating from about 1820-1900 was a time of personal expression. The impact of the French Revolution (1789-1794) set the stage for freedom and free-thinking individuals who set out in different artistic directions. Even in dress expressive beauty was portrayed. Women wore hoop skirts and decorative clothing with lace and/or embroidery. Men wore ruffled shirts, wide bow ties, and elegant clothes. Strong emphasis on emotion and imagination is found in literature, art, and architecture.

Romantic Keyboard Music

The music of the Romantic period often contains warm, beautiful melodies (so tuneful that many have been made into popular songs).

The accompaniment often colors and supports the melody.

from The Merry Farmer by Schumann

from A Little Song by Schumann

Frequently, expressive indications such as *espressivo* (expressively) and *dolce* (sweetly), etc. are used to aid the performer in interpreting the beautiful melodies. Color is added to the piano by more frequent use of pedal; pedal indications were used a great deal by Romantic composers.

1820-1900

Romantic Forms

During the Romantic period large works such as the sonata were still used, but intimate small works such as the waltz, rhapsody, impromptu, romance, ballade, nocturne, étude (study piece), and many others, were written with increasing frequency.

National folk music was used in works such as the polonaise and mazurka by the Polish composer, Chopin, and in the Hungarian rhapsody by Liszt, who was Hungarian.

The short works are often written in three-part song form: **A B A**.

The Piano in the Romantic Period

During the Romantic period the piano developed into a larger and more resonant instrument than the early piano in the Classical period. Development and perfection of the piano included a larger sound board, a heavier metal frame, thicker strings strung with more tension, a larger keyboard range, and a better pedal mechanism. All these factors aided in providing an instrument with a greater tone.

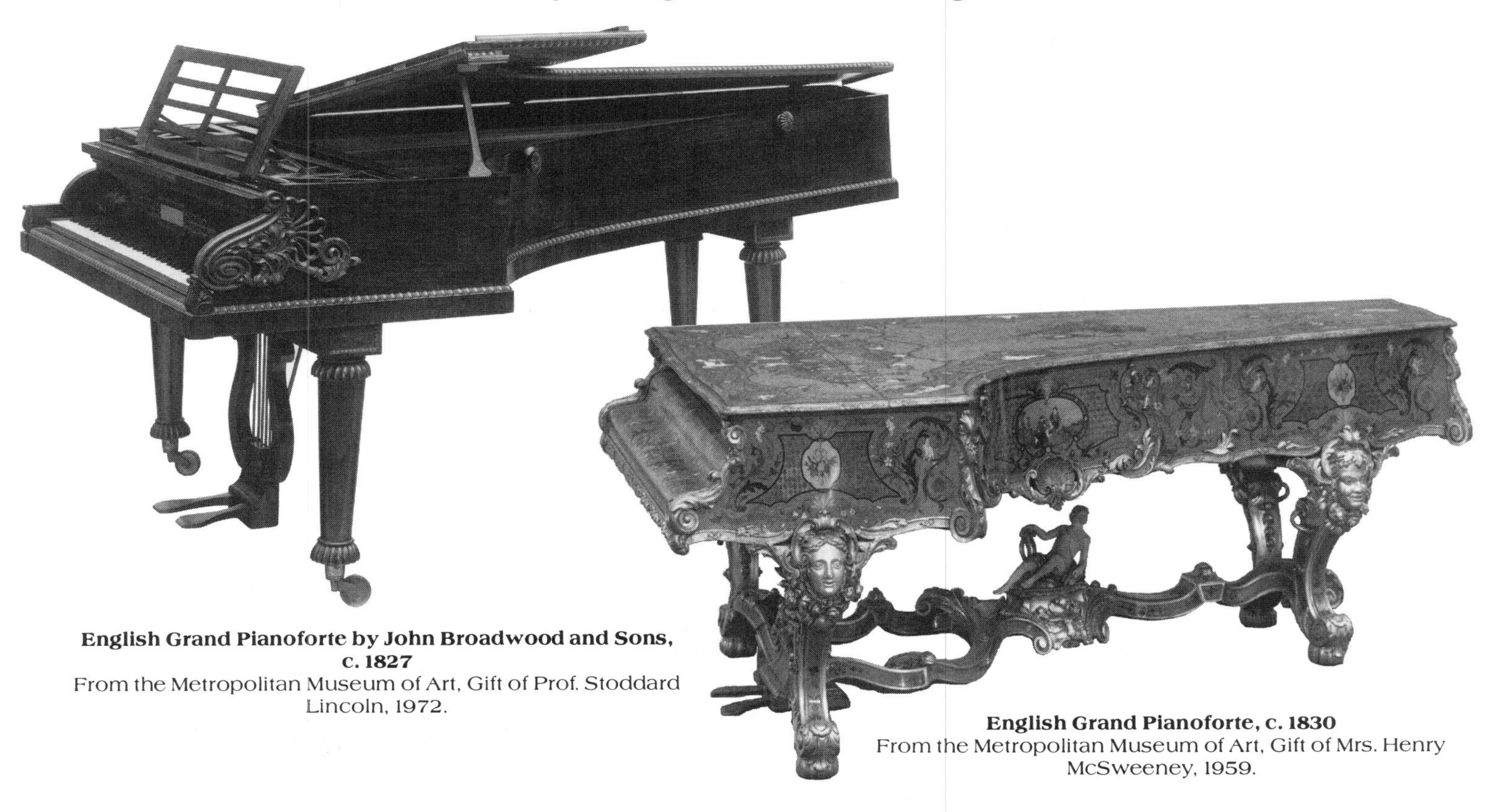

English Grand Pianoforte by John Broadwood and Sons, c. 1827
From the Metropolitan Museum of Art, Gift of Prof. Stoddard Lincoln, 1972.

English Grand Pianoforte, c. 1830
From the Metropolitan Museum of Art, Gift of Mrs. Henry McSweeney, 1959.

Romantic Composers

Ludwig van Beethoven (1770-1827) bridged the Classical and Romantic periods reflecting Classical influences in his early music and Romantic influences in his middle and later years. The most famous Romantic keyboard composers are Franz Schubert (1797-1828), Felix Mendelssohn (1809-1847), Frédéric Chopin (1810-1849), Robert Schumann (1810-1856), Franz Liszt (1811-1886), and Johannes Brahms (1833-1897). Other Romantic keyboard composers include César Franck (1822-1890), Modest Mussorgsky (1839-1881), Peter Ilyich Tchaikovsky (1840-1893), and Edvard Grieg (1843-1907).

Winter Storm

STYLE: ROMANTIC

JAMES BASTIEN

Name the chords as you learn this piece. Add the pedal *after* you can play it.

Song Without Words

STYLE: ROMANTIC

JAMES BASTIEN

Robert Schumann (1810-1856), a German composer, was a child prodigy who played the piano when he was six years old and composed his first piano pieces when he was seven. His mother wanted him to become a lawyer, but he chose a music career and was allowed to study with the famous piano teacher, Friedrich Wieck. In Leipzig in 1832 Schumann injured his hand trying to gain a better technique by tying his fourth finger to a mechanical device to strengthen it. Because that made a career as a pianist impossible, he devoted his energies to composition. In 1840 he married Clara Wieck (his piano teacher's daughter), against her father's wishes. Clara was a brilliant pianist who performed many of Schumann's works. Schumann published a magazine called *The New Music Journal.* In it he was the first to report the importance of Chopin and Brahms. In 1850 Schumann was appointed Musical Director for the city of Dusseldorf. He held that position until 1853 when signs of insanity, which had been evident as early as 1833, compelled him to resign. From 1854 he spent the remainder of his life in an asylum at his own request. His compositions include symphonies, many piano works, a piano concerto, chamber music, songs, and choral works. The pieces that follow are from the *Album for the Young* which Schumann wrote in 1848 as a birthday gift for his eldest daughter, Marie.

Soldier's March

from "Album for the Young"

STYLE: ROMANTIC

ROBERT SCHUMANN

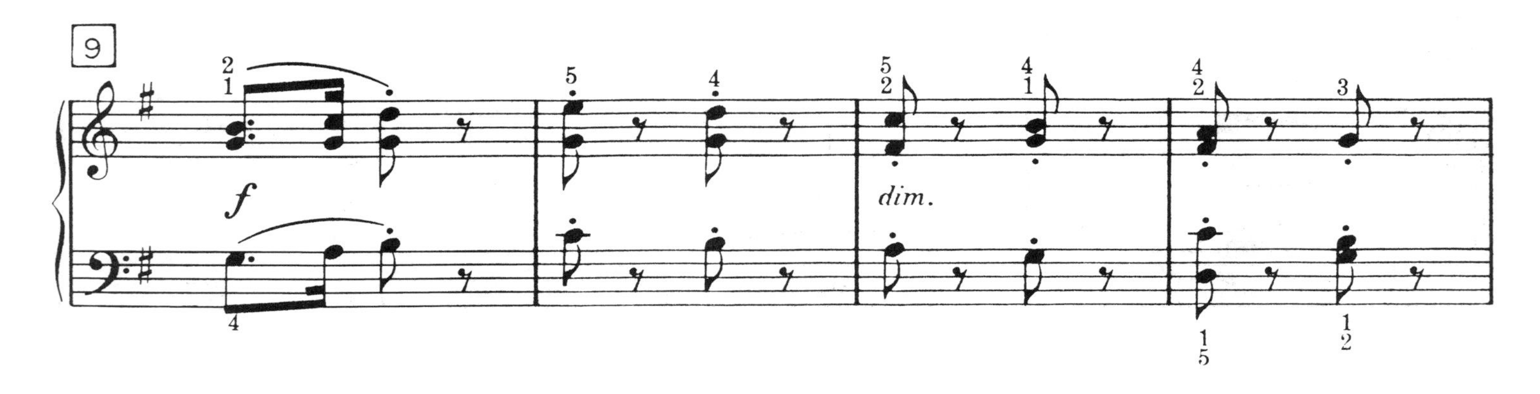

13
f
dim.
17
f
dim.
21
f
dim.
25
f
dim.
29
f
sfz
sfz

The Wild Horseman

from "Album for the Young"

STYLE: ROMANTIC

ROBERT SCHUMANN

Allegro con brio

mf sf 3 sf 6 sf sf 9 f sf

11
sf
14
17
mf
sf
sf
20
sf
23
sf

Franz Schubert (1797-1828), an Austrian composer, began violin lessons when he was eight. He was also given lessons for piano, organ, composition, and singing. He became a lead singer in the church choir in his 10th year. He followed his father's occupation as a teacher in an elementary school and taught unsuccessfully for three years from the age of 16 to 19. During these years he devoted his leisure time to composing songs, and in one year alone (1815) he composed 144 songs. He struggled continually to make a living, and although he was recognized as a composer of genius rank, he failed to obtain employment which would have provided a stable income. His income from composing was limited. He was disgracefully underpaid by his publishers, and he lived mostly in extreme poverty. Schubert, who had a great melodic gift, is the acknowledged creator of the Romantic art song *(lied);* and he wrote over six hundred songs *(lieder).* He also wrote nine symphonies (including the famous "Unfinished" Symphony), religious works, choral music, operas, chamber music, and numerous piano solo and duet works.

Écossaise

Op. 18, No. 4

Little Waltz

STYLE: ROMANTIC

JANE SMISOR BASTIEN

Tempo di Valse

mp

6

11

mf

16

dim.

p

THE CONTEMPORARY

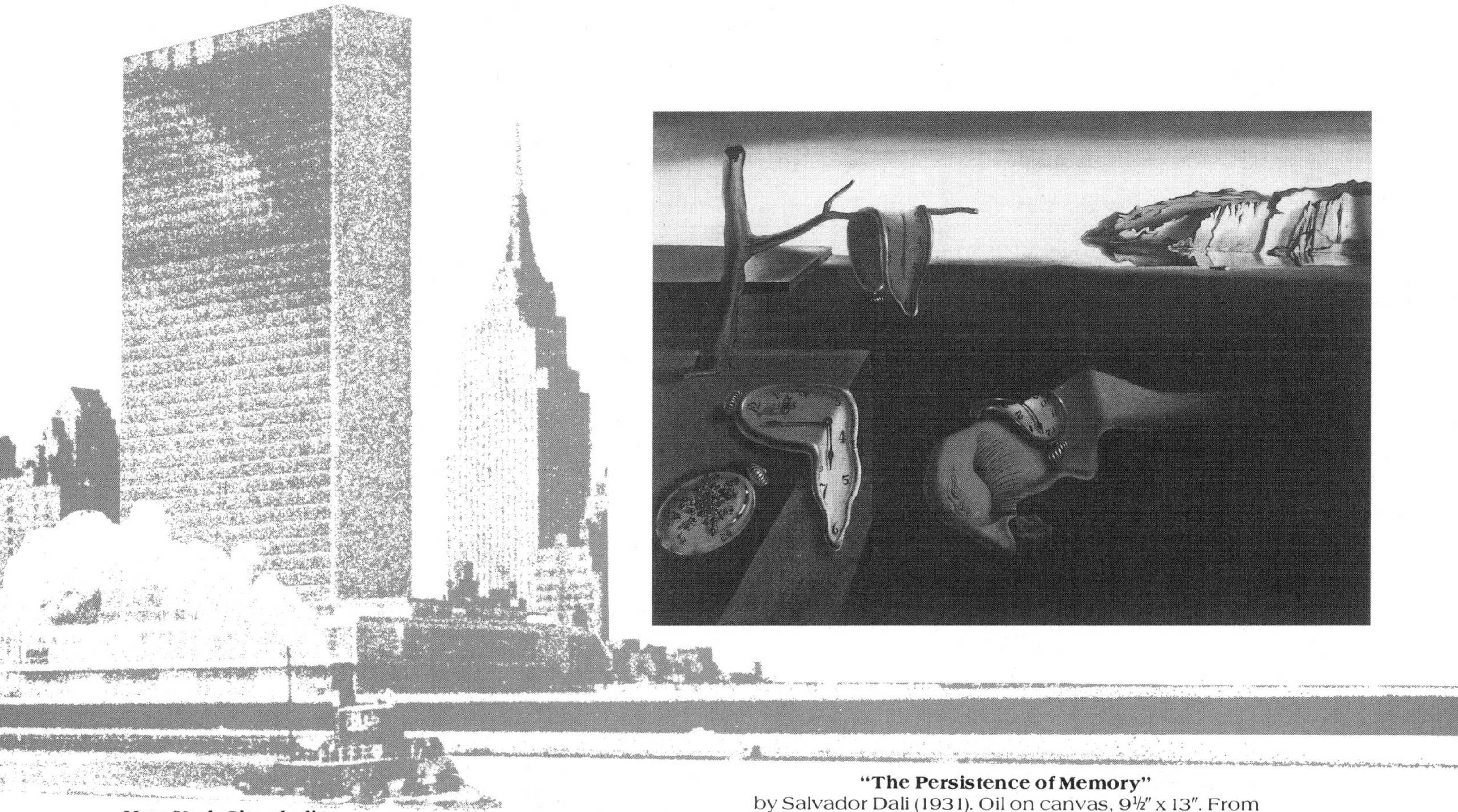

New York City skyline

"The Persistence of Memory"
by Salvador Dali (1931). Oil on canvas, 9½" x 13". From
The Museum of Modern Art, New York. Given Anonymously.

Contemporary Style

The Contemporary period, beginning about 1900, reflects our modern, mechanized, atomic age. Contemporary music is often angular and dissonant, portraying anxiety and the "clash and clang" of modern city life. Compared to the Romantic period, modern dress is practical, simple, and tailored. New synthetic man-made materials are frequently used in place of natural materials such as wool or cotton. Likewise, experiments with "synthetic" electronic music have produced totally new mediums for musical expression. The art and architecture of our period contain elements ranging from angular shapes to sleek, functional lines.

Contemporary Keyboard Music

The keyboard music in the Contemporary period frequently contains new sounds such as the whole-tone scale (example: D, E, F♯, G♯, A♯, C) and twelve-tone music (twelve different tones arranged in a particular sequence). Also, the music may include changing meters and an irregular number of measures (3, 5, or 7) in phrases.

from Spiders by Bastien

The accompaniment in the Contemporary period may include some dissonant chords, used for color, that do not belong to the notes in the melody.

from Follow the Leader by Bartók

PERIOD 1900-PRESENT

Contemporary Forms

Although standard forms from other eras are used, today's composers use them in personal ways to reflect their own styles. Debussy used the prelude, étude, and suite; Bartók used the forms of the bagatelle, sonata, suite, rondo, folk songs and dances; and Kabalevsky used the prelude, variations, sonata, rondo, and prelude and fugue. Brilliant display pieces such as the toccata and étude are common forms among contemporary composers as well.

The Piano in the Contemporary Period

The Contemporary piano is even larger and more resonant than the piano in the Romantic period. The modern grand has a brilliant tone necessary for projection in today's large concert halls.

Grand Piano
Grand pianos are available in several lengths ranging roughly from four to nine feet. In general, the larger the piano the better the sound.

Electronic Piano
Electronic pianos range from portable keyboards of a few octaves to instruments that look like a spinet, but have headsets for the player's use. The models shown are especially for class piano instruction.

Contemporary Composers

Within the "modern" era great style variations are found, ranging from composers such as Sergei Rachmaninoff (1873-1943) and others writing in a somewhat romantic style, to composer Claude Debussy (1862-1918) and Maurice Ravel (1875-1937) who wrote in a mildly contemporary style. George Gershwin (1898-1937) and others wrote music combining elements of jazz in a contemporary, individual style. Composers who developed new concepts of melody-tonality-rhythm include Béla Bartók (1881-1945), Igor Stravinsky (1882-1971), Sergei Prokofiev (1891-1952), Aaron Copland (1900-1990), Dmitri Kabalevsky (1904-1987), Dmitri Shostakovich (1906-1975), and Samuel Barber (1900-1981).

Fog

STYLE: CONTEMPORARY

JAMES BASTIEN

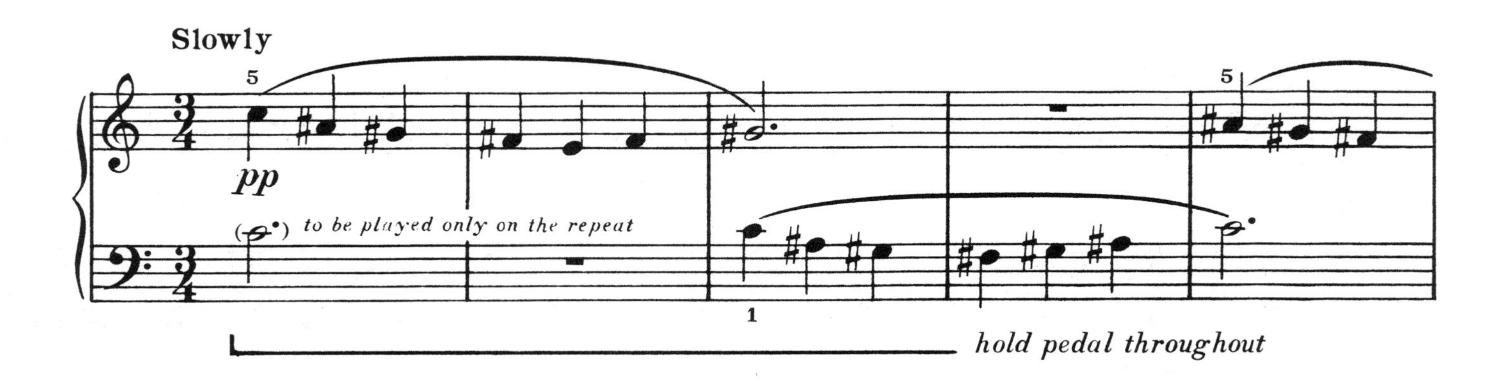

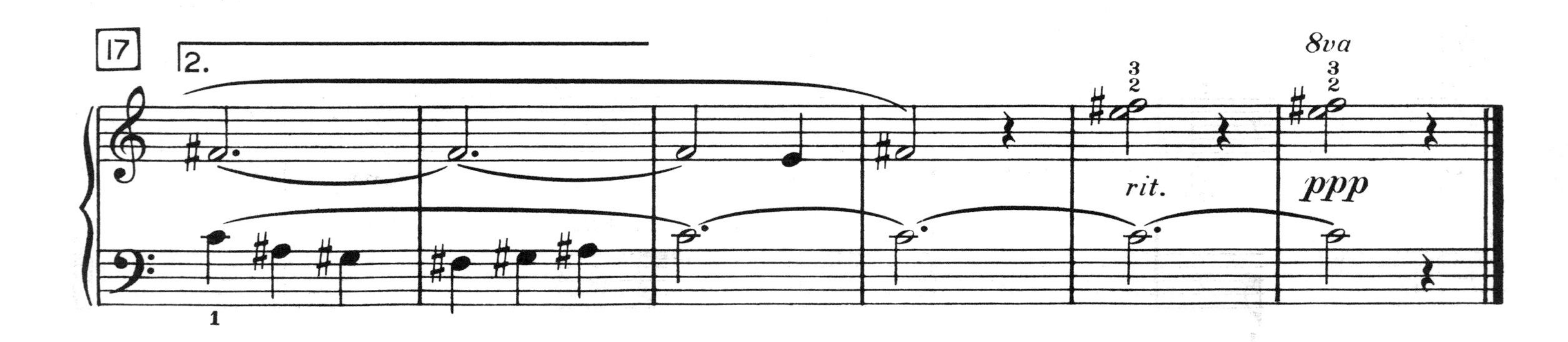

Caravan

STYLE: CONTEMPORARY

JAMES BASTIEN

Dmitri Kabalevsky (1904-1987), a Russian composer, was born in St. Petersburg. He began to play the piano by ear when he was six years old, but he did not begin formal lessons until he was 14. At that time his family moved to Moscow, and he entered the Scriabin School of Music studying piano and composition. When he was 21 he entered the Moscow Conservatory and was such a brilliant student that upon graduation he was invited to become a Professor of Composition. In addition, the Russian government hired him to teach in the Scriabin School, where he wrote teaching materials for the children. Among the best known works for young students are his piano pieces (*Children's Pieces*, Op. 27; *24 Pieces for Children*, Op. 39; and *Variations*, Op. 40) and youth concertos (the best known being the *Youth Concerto for Piano, No. 3*). In addition to composing and teaching Kabalevsky has been a conductor, music critic, musicologist, and has toured as a pianist. He has written symphonies, concertos, ballets, chamber music, advanced piano pieces and music for radio programs, movies, and stage plays.

Scherzo

from "24 Pieces for Children" Op. 39

Waltz

from "24 Pieces for Children" Op. 39

Béla Bartók (1881-1945), a Hungarian composer, studied the piano with his mother as a child. He completed his musical training at the Franz Liszt Academy in Budapest studying piano with Istvan Thoman, who had been a pupil of Liszt. Bartók was a brilliant pianist, and he made concert tours throughout Europe. His first tour in the United States was in 1927. He returned to Budapest where he was Professor of Piano at the Conservatory. Because of political difficulties, he came to the United States in 1940 where he lived until his death. He spent many years collecting Hungarian and Slavic folk music, much of which is reflected in his music. He wrote more than 100 piano pieces for youngsters in collections such as *First Term at the Piano, For Children,* and *Ten Easy Pieces.* His works include advanced piano music, orchestral works, concertos, choral music, chamber music, songs, and music for the stage.

Follow the Leader

from "For Children"

STYLE: CONTEMPORARY

BÉLA BARTÓK

24
f
p
29
Tempo I
p
35
41
p
pp
p
47
pp
rit.

Lilacs in the Moonlight

STYLE: CONTEMPORARY

JAMES BASTIEN

18
a tempo
f
22
26
mf
30
f
dim.
34
8va
rit.
p
8va

The toccata is a spirited keyboard piece displaying exciting technique. The modern toccata is percussive using a sharp, biting staccato touch. (*Toccata Breve* means short toccata.)

Toccata Breve

STYLE: CONTEMPORARY

JAMES BASTIEN

20
ff
p
ff
24
p
cresc.
f
28
dim.
mf
33
38
cresc.
ff
8va

REFERENCE

This six-page section presents the basic theory covered in THE BASTIEN PIANO LIBRARY through Level 4 and may serve as review or reference.

Key Signatures

A key signature consists of the sharps or flats at the beginning of each staff. A key signature indicates two things:

1. The notes to be sharped or flatted throughout the entire piece.
2. The main key (tonality) of the piece.

Sharps and flats are always written in the same order on the staff.
The order of sharps is: F C G D A E B

The order of flats is: B E A D G C F
(Note: The sequence of flats is in reverse order of the sharps.)

The steps for identifying major sharp key signatures are:

1. Determine what the last sharp to the right is.
2. Go *up* to the very next note (one half step).
   That is the name of the major key.

The steps for identifying major flat key signatures are:

1. Determine what the next-to-the-last flat is.
2. That is the name of the major key, with the exceptions of the key of C (no sharps or flats) and the key of F (one flat only).

Every key signature applies to two keys, one in major and one in minor. A key signature with one sharp could represent G major or its relative,E minor. The minor key is two alphabet letters lower (three half steps) than the major key name.

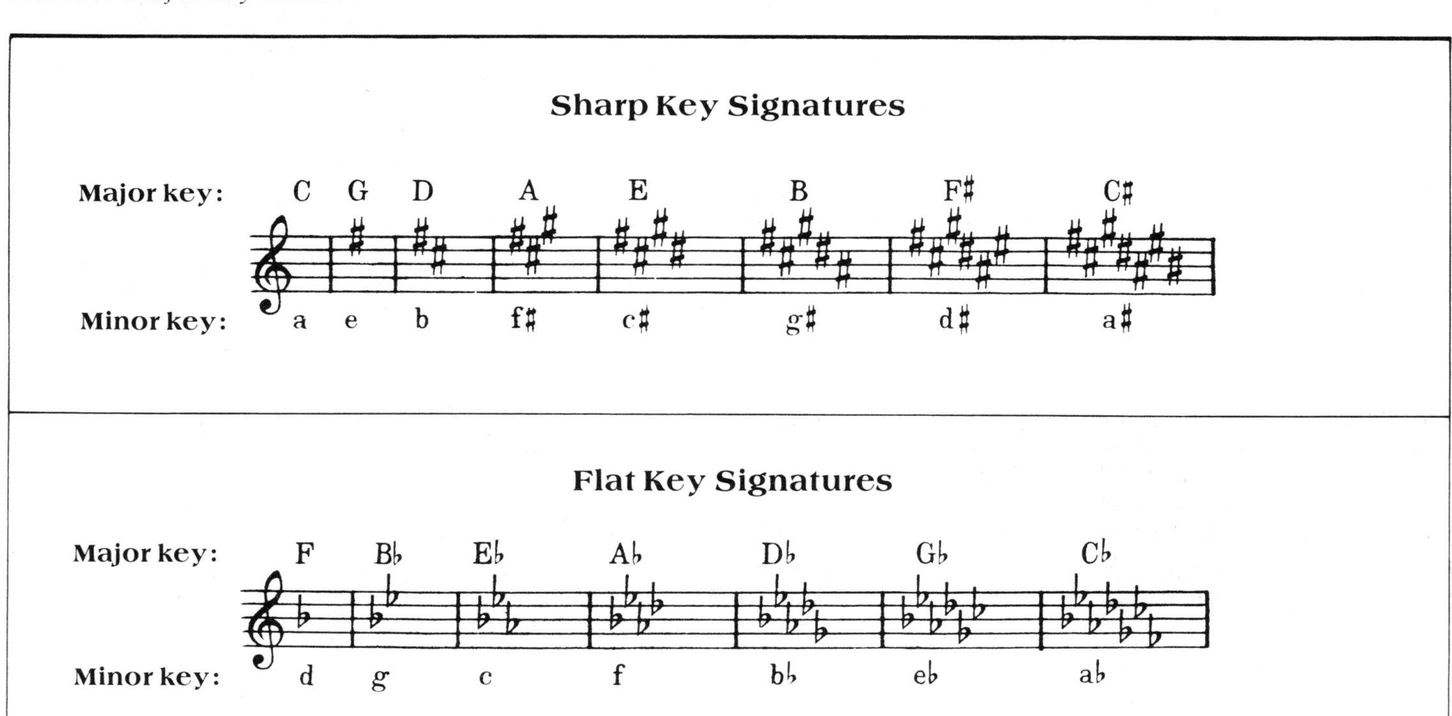

Half Step, Whole Step

The terms half step and whole step are used to *measure distances* on the piano keyboard.

Major Scales

There are eight tones in a major scale called scale *degrees*. The scale degrees are arranged in a pattern of *whole steps* (1) and *half steps* (1/2). Roman numerals may be used to name scale degrees. Also, music terms may be used to name scale degrees: I, Tonic; ii, Supertonic; iii, Mediant; IV, Subdominant; V, Dominant; vi, Submediant; vii°, Leading Tone.

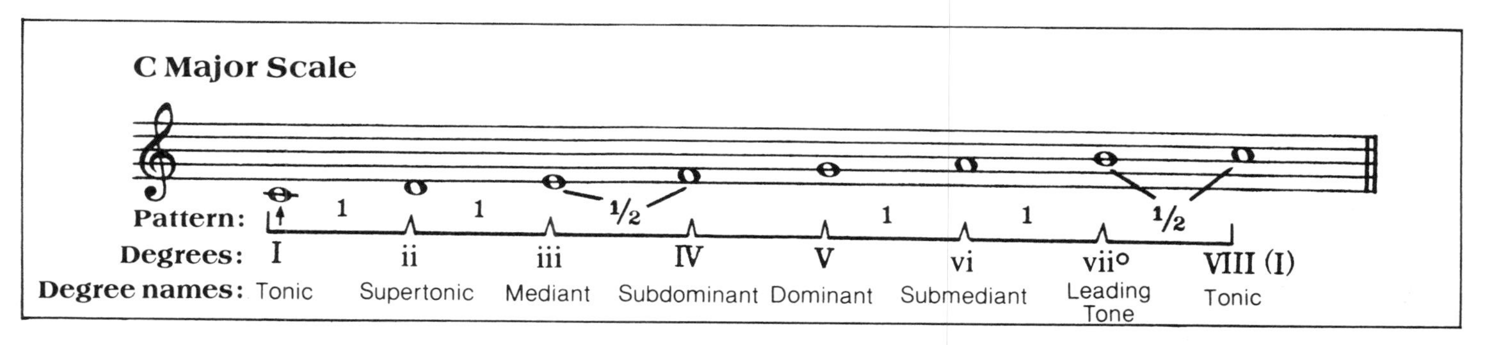

Minor Scales

Minor scales are related to major scales because they have the *same* key signature; they are called *relative* minors. The three forms of relative minor scales are *natural, harmonic, melodic.*

The **natural minor scale** uses exactly the same tones as the relative major scale, but it starts on the sixth tone of the major scale.

A Natural Minor Scale (relative of C major)

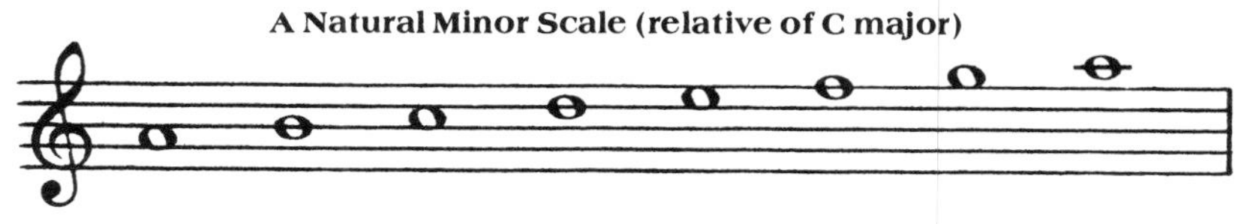

The **harmonic minor scale** uses the notes of the natural minor scale, but the seventh tone (degree) is raised a half step. The raised seventh must be written in as an accidental, because it is not in the key signature.

A Harmonic Minor Scale (relative of C major)

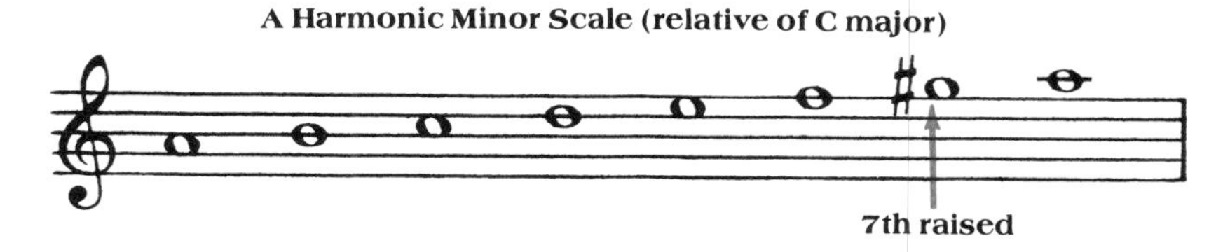

The **melodic minor scale** uses the notes of the natural minor scale, but the sixth and seventh tones are raised a half step going up. The sixth and seventh tones are lowered going down.

A Melodic Minor Scale (relative of C major)

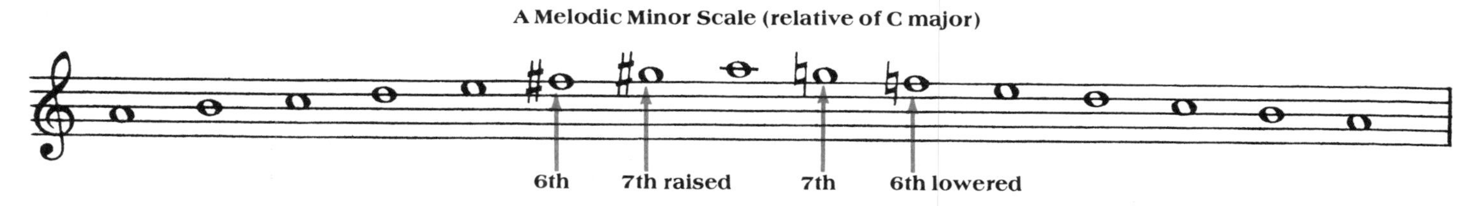

Intervals

An interval is the pitch relation or *distance* between two tones. The various types of intervals are major, minor, perfect, augmented, and diminished.

Major and Perfect Intervals

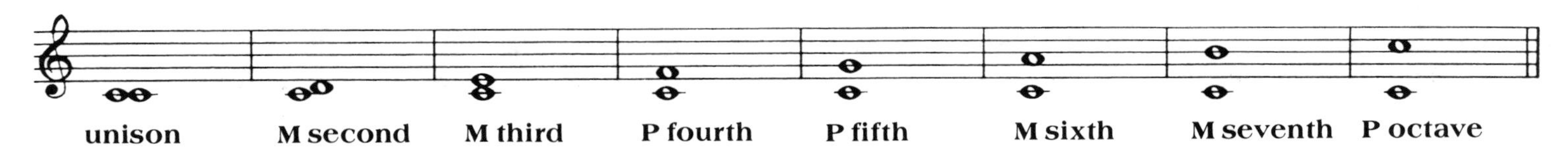

Altered Intervals

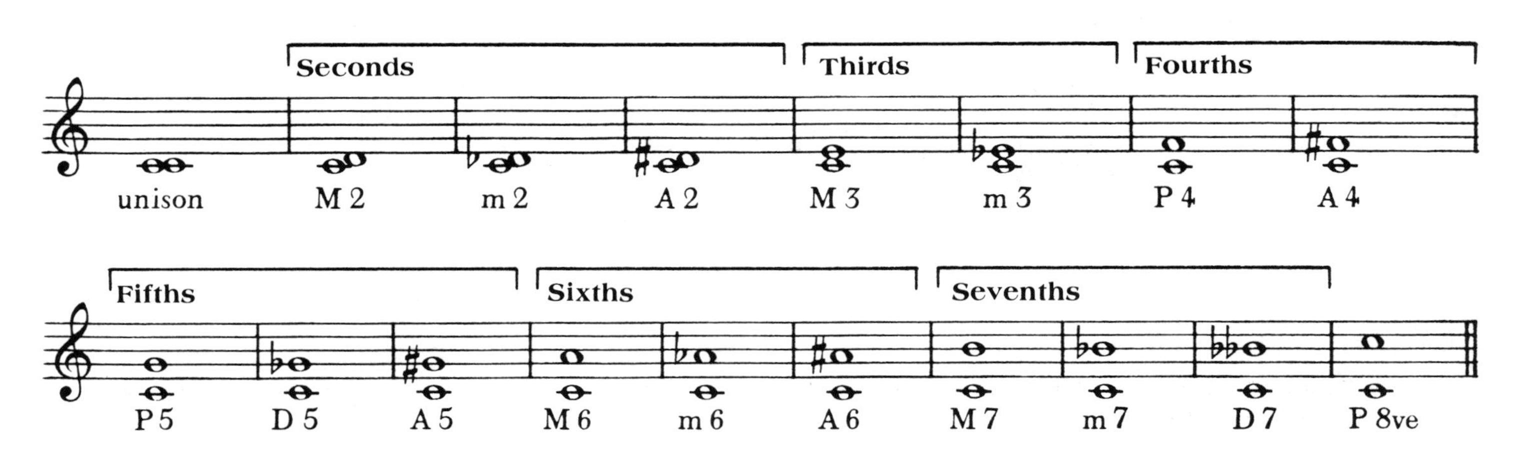

Chords

A chord is a combination of simultaneously-sounding tones. Chords provide *harmony* in music. Chords are "spelled" from the lowest tone upwards (C E G, not G E C) and are formed from musical alphabet skips (C E G, C E G B, etc.). The notes within chords form intervals. A triad (a three-note chord) has a root, third, and fifth; a seventh chord (a four-note chord) has a root, third, fifth, and seventh.

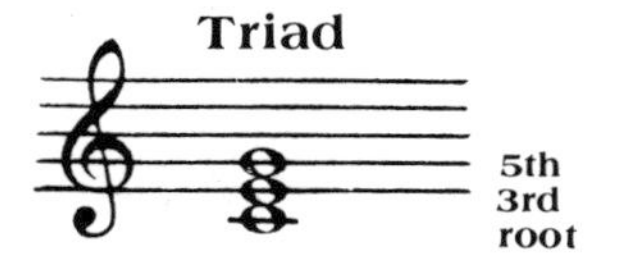

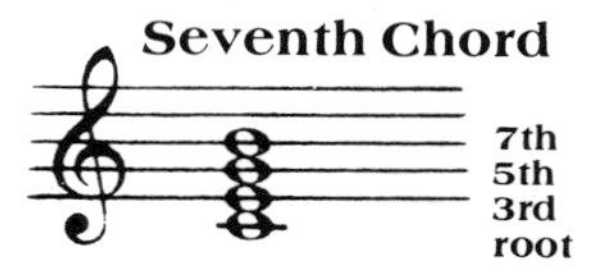

Chord symbols frequently are used to name the *type* of chord (major, minor, etc.). A chord symbol is the letter name of the chord (in root position) printed in music, usually above the melody: C, F, Dm, G Aug, etc. A single capital letter refers to a major chord (C = C major); a capital letter with an "m" after it refers to a minor chord (Cm = C minor); a capital letter with "Aug" after it refers to an augmented chord (C Aug = C augmented); a capital letter with "dim" after it refers to a diminished chord (C dim = C diminished).

These four different triads are used most frequently: *major* triad, *minor* triad, *augmented* triad, and *diminished* triad.

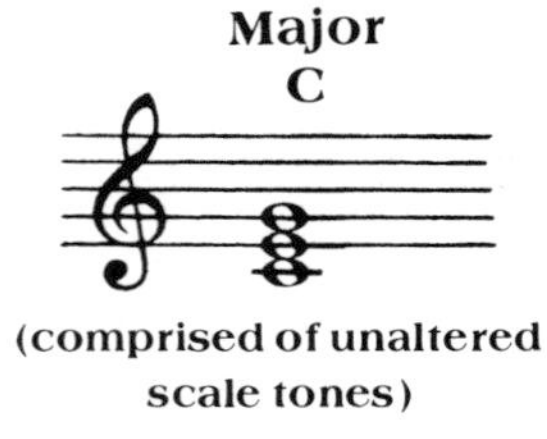

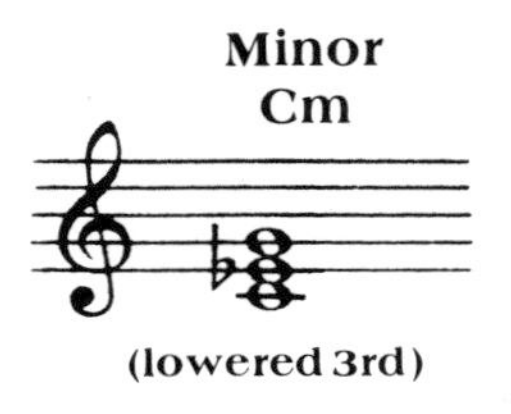

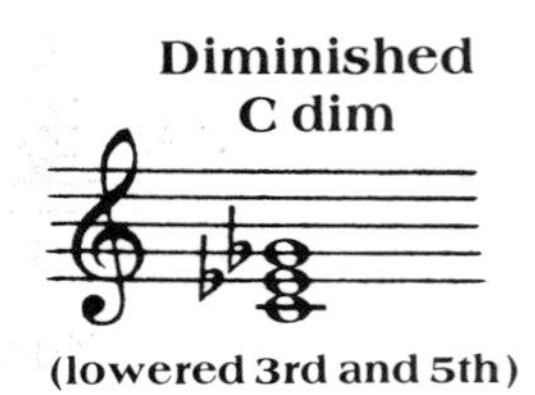

A chord can be constructed on each note of the scale. Triads I, IV, and V in major scales are called *primary triads* and are major. Triads ii, iii, and vi are minor. Triad vii° is diminished.

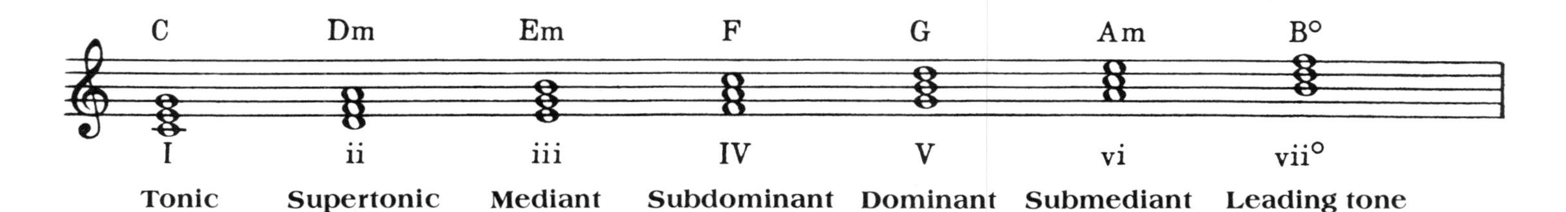

Inversions of Chords

Any chord may be *inverted* (rearranged). A triad is inverted by moving the root note to the top or middle.

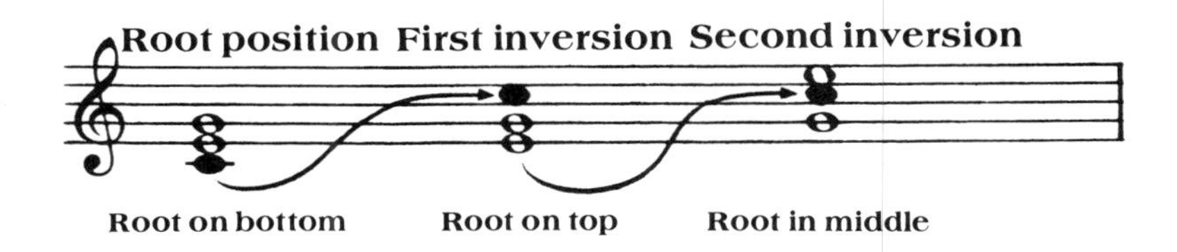

Dominant 7th Chord

The dominant seventh chord is built on the *fifth* tone of the scale. The dominant seventh chord has a root, third, fifth, and seventh.

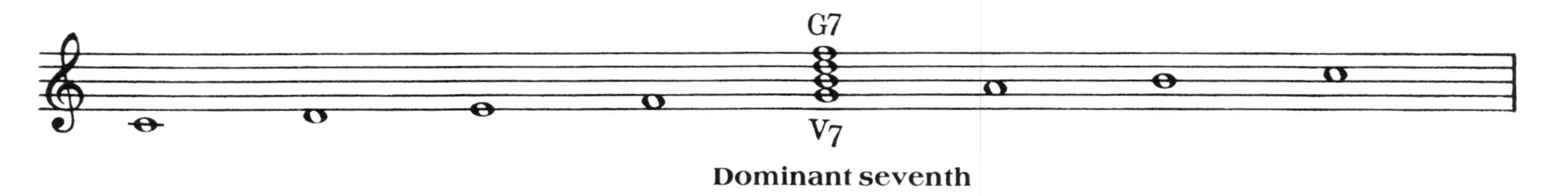

The dominant seventh chord has four positions because it is a four-note chord: root position, first inversion, second inversion, third inversion.

Each inversion of the dominant seventh chord has an interval of a *second*. The *root* of the inverted chord is the *top* note of the interval that is a second. Understanding this will aid in identifying inverted seventh chords.

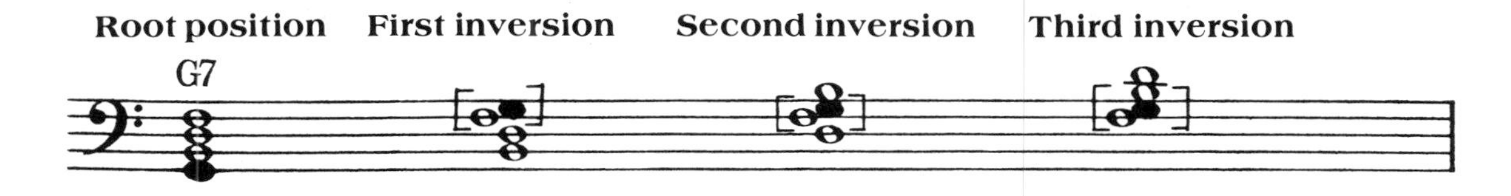

Playing Primary Chords on the Piano

For harmonization, primary chords are frequently played on the piano in this manner: I, root position; IV, second inversion; V7, first inversion (with the fifth omitted).

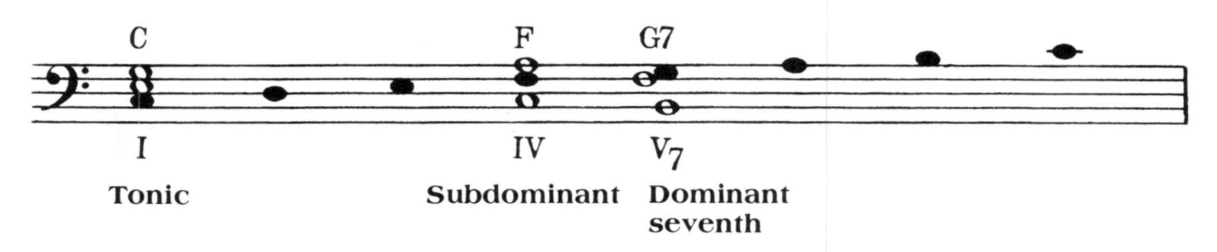

Notes, Rests, Basic Rhythms ($\frac{2}{4}$, $\frac{3}{4}$, $\frac{4}{4}$)

Notes	Rests (indicate measured silence)
whole note	whole rest
half note	half rest
quarter note	quarter rest
eighth note	eighth rest
sixteenth note	sixteenth rest

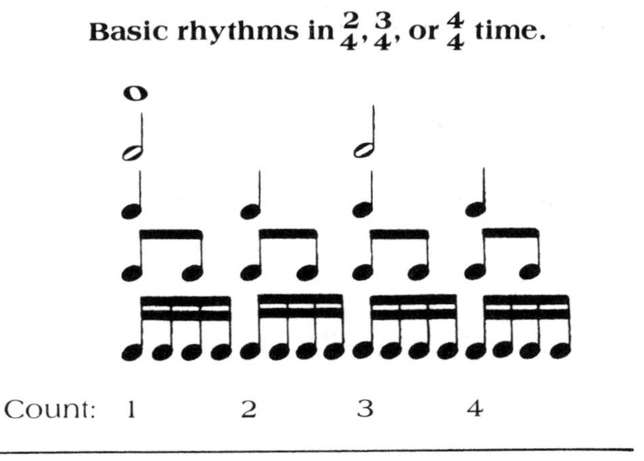

A dot after a note increases its value by one-half:

= 2   = 3
= 1   = 1½
= ½   = ¾

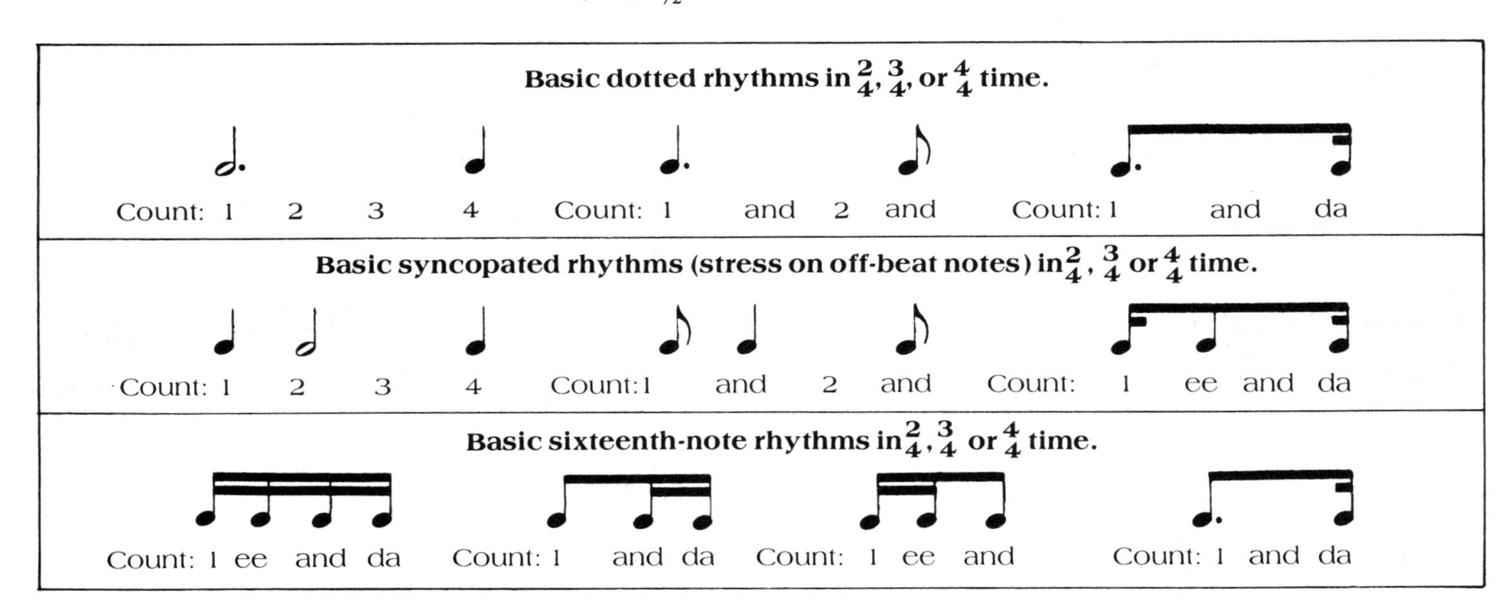

Notes, Rests, Basic Rhythms ($\frac{6}{8}$)

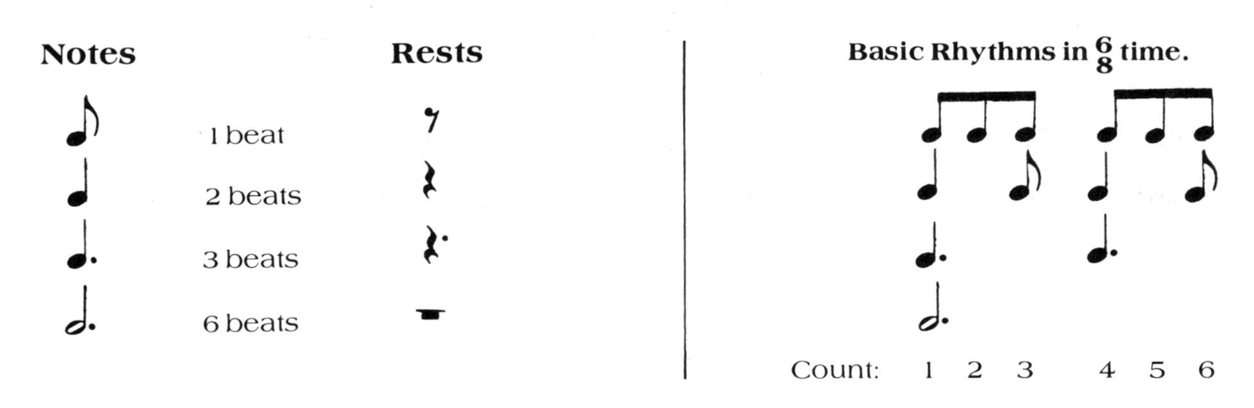

Circle of Keys

This diagram is called the circle of keys. The sharps are arranged from the top, moving clockwise. The flats are arranged from the top, moving counter-clockwise.

There are 15 major keys: 7 sharp keys, 7 flat keys, and 1 key with no sharps or flats.

There are 15 relative minor keys.

The keys with two names at the bottom of the circle are called enharmonic.

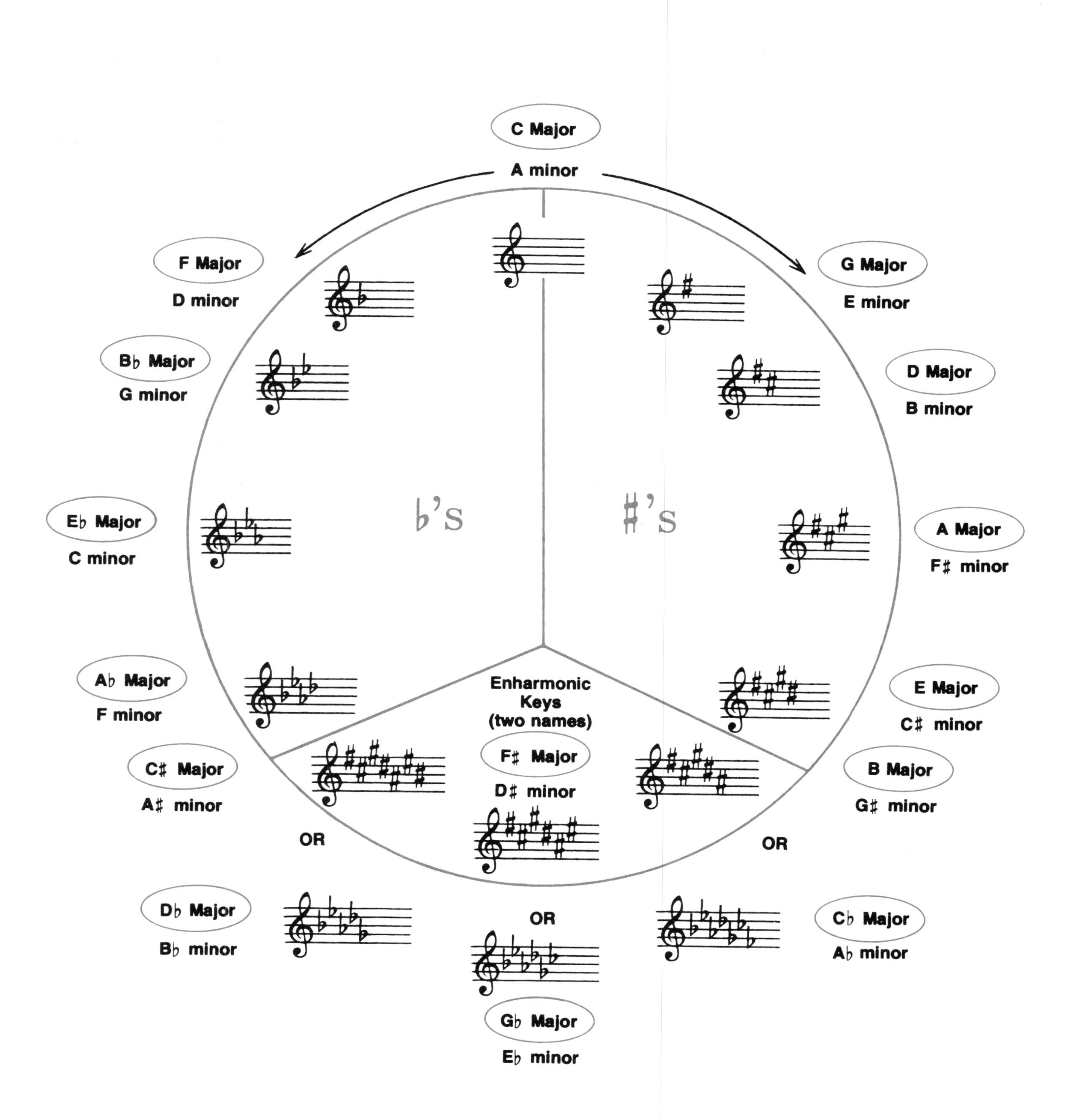

Chronological List of Keyboard Composers

Baroque Period (1600-1750)

Jean Baptiste Lully, French (1632-1687)
Henry Purcell, English (1658-1695)
François Couperin, French (1668-1733)
Georg Philipp Telemann, German (1681-1767)
Jean-Philippe Rameau, French (1683-1764)
Johann Sebastian Bach, German (1685-1750)
Domenico Scarlatti, Italian (1685-1757)
George Frideric Handel, German (1685-1759)

Classical Period (1775-1825)

Wilhelm Friedemann Bach, German (1710-1784)
Carl Philipp Emanuel Bach, German (1714-1788)
Johann Christian Bach, German (1735-1782)
Johann Philipp Kirnberger, German (1721-1783)
Joseph Haydn, Austrian (1732-1809)
Muzio Clementi, Italian (1752-1832)
Wolfgang Amadeus Mozart, Austrian (1756-1791)
Daniel Gottlieb Türk, German (1756-1813)
Ludwig van Beethoven, German (1770-1827)
Antonio Diabelli, Italian (1781-1858)
Friedrich Kuhlau, German (1786-1832)

Romantic Period (1800-1900)

Franz Schubert, German (1797-1828)
Felix Mendelssohn, German (1809-1847)
Friedrich Burgmüller, German (1806-1874)
Frédéric Chopin, Polish (1810-1849)
Robert Schumann, German (1810-1856)
Franz Liszt, Hungarian (1811-1886)
Stephen Heller, German (1813-1888)
Fritz Spindler, German (1817-1905)
Theodor Kullak, German (1818-1882)
Louis Kohler, German (1820-1886)
Cornelius Gurlitt, German (1820-1901)
César Franck, French (1822-1890)
Johannes Brahms, German (1833-1897)
Camille Saint-Saëns, French (1835-1921)
Modest Mussorgsky, Russian (1839-1881)
Peter Tchaikowsky, Russian (1840-1893)
Edvard Grieg, Norwegian (1844-1908)
Vladimir Rebikoff, Russian (1866-1920)

Contemporary Period (1900-   )

Edward MacDowell, American (1861-1908)
Claude Debussy, French (1862-1918)
Alexander Gretchaninoff, Russian (1864-1956)
Erik Satie, French (1866-1925)
Amy Beach, (1867-1944)
Alexander Scriabin, Russian (1872-1915)
Max Reger, German (1873-1916)
Sergei Rachmaninoff, Russian (1873-1943)
Arnold Schoenberg, Austrian (1874-1951)
Maurice Ravel, French (1875-1937)
Manuel de Falla, Spanish (1876-1946)
Ernst von Dohnányi, Hungarian (1877-1960)
Ernest Bloch, Swiss (1880-1959)
Béla Bartók, Hungarian (1881-1945)
Joaquin Turina, Spanish (1882-1949)
Igor Stravinsky, Russian (1882-1971)
Anton Webern, Austrian (1883-1945)
Alfredo Casella, Italian (1883-1947)
Alban Berg, Austrian (1885-1935)
Heitor Villa-Lobos, Brazilian (1881-1959)
Jacques Ibert, French (1890-1962)
Sergei Prokofieff, Russian (1891-1953)
Darius Milhaud, French (1892-1974)
Paul Hindemith, German (1895-1963)
George Gershwin, American (1898-1937)
Francis Poulenc, French (1899-1963)
Alexander Tcherepnin, Russian (1899-1977)
Aaron Copland, American (1900-1990)
Ernst Krenek, Austrian (1900-1991)
Aram Khachaturian, Russian (1903-1978)
Dmitri Kabalevsky, Russian (1904-1987)
Dmitri Shostakovich, Russian (1906-1975)
Paul Creston, American (1906-1985)
Ross Lee Finney, American (1906-1997)
Elliot Carter, American (1908-   )
Samuel Barber, American (1910-1981)
Gian Carlo Menotti, American (1911-2007)
Norman Dello Joio, American (1913-2008)
Vincent Persichetti, American (1915-1987)
David Diamond, American (1915-2005)
Alberto Ginastera, Argentine (1916-1983)
Leonard Bernstein, American (1918-1990)
Ned Rorem, American (1923-   )
Robert Starer, American (1924-2001)
Carlisle Floyd, American (1926-   )
Robert Muczynski, American (1929-   )

Glossary

Absolute pitch
The ability to correctly identify sounds (pitches) heard.

Acoustics
The science of sound.

Arrangement
The adaptation of a composition for an instrument or instruments other than those specified in the original form.

Atonality
The absence of tonal (key) feeling.

Augmentation
The lengthening of note values.

Bitonality
The use of two different keys simultaneously.

Cadenza
An extended solo passage to display the performer's technical skill; usually appears in a concerto before the conclusion of the first movement.

Chord
A simultaneous sounding of three or more tones.

Chromatic
Tones foreign to a key. A scale comprised of semitones.

Concerto
A composition for one or more solo instruments with orchestra.

Consonance
A state of relative rest between tones that produces an agreeable effect.

Contrapuntal
In the style of counterpoint. Two or more individual melodic parts combined at the same time.

Counterpoint
"Note against note." The art of writing independent melodies against each other.

Development
The evolution or elaboration of a melody or motive.

Development section
The middle portion in a sonata-allegro movement where the themes and motives are elaborated on.

Diatonic
The natural succession of tones within a scale, excluding chromatic alterations.

Dissonance
A combination of tones that produces unrest and generally creates a disagreeable effect.

Embellishment
Melodic ornamentation consisting of trills, grace notes, runs, etc.

Enharmonic
The same pitch, but with two possible ways of naming and notating: F♯ and G♭.

Ensemble
Any combination or group of singers and/or instrumentalists.

Exposition
The initial section of a musical form in which the basic thematic material is presented. The first portion of a sonata-allegro movement (exposition, development, recapitulation).

Form
The structure of a musical composition.

Glissando
Gliding or sliding. In keyboard music, playing a series of keys by dragging a finger (or fingers) along the keyboard.

Harmony
Consonant sounds that produce a pleasing whole. The science of chord and chordal progressions.

Homophony, homophonic
A musical style in which the melody predominates and the accompaniment is subordinate.

Linear motion
Scale-wise (step-wise) motion. Horizontal motion.

Metronome
A device to indicate the exact tempo of a composition. Invented by John Maelzel in 1815, the metronome indicates any desired number of beats per second.

Motive
A brief fragment of a musical theme or subject which may have special melodic and/or rhythmic character.

Movement
A main section of a large work such as a first movement of a sonata, concerto or symphony.

Percussive effect
Strident, sharp, biting sound.

Phrase
A natural division of the melodic line, punctuated by some form of cadence (melodic, harmonic, or rhythmic close).

Polyphony, polyphonic
Simultaneous sounding of two or more melodies.

Polytonal, polytonality
The use of several different keys simultaneously.

Recapitulation
The reprise or restatement of material already presented. The third portion of the first movement in sonata-allegro form (exposition, development, recapitulation).

Sonority
Richness or fullness of sound.

Tonality
The gravitation of a musical composition around a key or tonal center.

Touch
The manner in which the keys of the piano are depressed to produce different tone qualities.

Virtuosity
Brilliant display of technical facility.

Music Dictionary

TERM	ABBREVIATION or Sign	MEANING
Accelerando	*accel.*	gradually increase speed
Accent sign	>	stress and play louder
Alla Breve	₵	$\frac{2}{2}$ time; two strong beats to the measure
Alla marcia		in march time
Allegretto		moderately fast
Allegro		fast ("cheerful")
Andante		walking speed
Animato		lively, animated
A Tempo		return to the original speed
Cantabile		in a singing style
Coda		an added ending
Con		with
Con brio		with spirit
Con spirito		with spirit
Crescendo	*cresc.*	play gradually louder
Da Capo al Fine	*D. C. al Fine*	return to the beginning and play to the word *"Fine"*
Decrescendo	*decresc.*	play gradually softer
Del Segno al Fine	*D. S. al Fine*	return to the sign (𝄋) and play to the word *"Fine"*
Diminuendo	*dim.*	play gradually softer
Dolce		sweetly
Espressivo		with expression
Fermata	𝄐	hold the note (or notes) longer
Fine		the end
Forte	*f*	loud
Fortissimo	*ff*	very loud
Grazioso		gracefully
Largo		very slowly
Legato		smooth, connected tones
Lento		very slowly
Mezzo Forte	*mf*	moderately loud
Mezzo Piano	*mp*	moderately soft
Moderato		a moderate speed
Molto		much, very
Non		not
Octave sign	*8va*	play eight scale degrees higher (one octave) when the sign is above the notes; play eight scale degrees lower when the sign is below the notes
	15ma	play two octaves higher than written
Pianissimo	*pp*	very soft
Piano	*p*	soft
Piu		more
Poco a poco		little by little
Presto		very fast
Repeat sign	𝄇	go back and play again
Ritardando	*rit.*	play gradually slower
Scherzando		playfully
Sforzando	*sfz*	a sudden strong accent
Simile		similar
Staccato		short, disconnected tones
Subito		suddenly
Tempo		rate of speed
Tenuto sign	–	held, sustained for full value
Tie		connects two notes on the same line or space; hold the notes for their combined value.
Vivace		lively, quick
Vivo		lively